Daniel Lang

THE MAN

IN THE THICK LEAD SUIT

New York

OXFORD UNIVERSITY PRESS

1954

COPYRIGHT 1954 BY DANIEL LANG

Library of Congress Catalogue Card Number: 54-10001

SECOND PRINTING, SEPTEMBER 1954

The chapters of this book originally appeared in The New Yorker *in slightly different form. Copyright 1949, 1951, 1952, 1953, 1954 by Daniel Lang.*

PRINTED IN THE UNITED STATES OF AMERICA

*

To Bella and Sam

∗

INTRODUCTION

DANIEL LANG is the quietly superb reporter for *The New Yorker,* in which these chapters originally appeared. He is not a philosopher, so he does not attempt to answer the question whether man's incapacity for sustained fear or wonderment is our fatal defect or the built-in governor preventing our final self-destruction. I have seen it operate in both directions, and I do not know what the answer is. I remember Londoners in 1937 unable to grasp the notion that London could ever lie in ruins, so, of course, it did. I remember Calcutta bureaucrats in the Bengal famine of 1943 unable to grasp the fact that a million human beings were dying in gutters and sewers and attics all around them, so, of course, life went on.

After watching one spectacular atomic bomb burst at Yucca Flat, Lang felt vaguely disturbed that he had not felt more disturbed. A day or so later, the physicist in charge, Dr. Alvin C. Graves, suggested that it was not indifference to the bomb that had troubled him but awareness that human imagination has its limits.

In a sense, this is what the chapters in this book are all about. Wonder and fear cannot endure very long. We are pulled back to the known and manageable. The peasants on the slopes of Vesuvius and Etna form a new garden wall from the ridge of the latest cooling lava; the Las Vegas croupiers take precautions lest the latest test blast cause the roulette ball to bounce out of one number to another; the hydrogen bomb test is casually labeled "Mike"; the horsey set at Aiken, South Carolina, is a little annoyed lest the new H-bomb installation interfere with the drag hunt; the word "megadeath" already comes easily to the tongue; the Air Force has moved from "spot bombing" to "area bombing" and once it is equipped with Hydrogen bombs, I have no doubt its mimeograph operators will soon become familiar with some routine hieroglyph such as "UD" meaning "urban depletion."

It should be a little breath-taking that a Navajo sheepherder was merely riding to the Rattlesnake Trading Post for cigarettes when he came upon one of the most tremendous uranium deposits on the continent; breath-taking that picknicking families in Dakota take their Geiger counter along with the thermos jug; that proprietors of Las Vegas tourist traps feel annoyed when the newest blast isn't bigger and better than the last; that the Brothers Alsop now write about a "hatful" of atomic bombs for Indo-China, without the quotation marks.

It should be, but it isn't. And it isn't, because it can't be. We could survive even the worst, if we moved our cities underground, but we are not going to do that. We will not, because we have an unspoken, almost unconscious, foreknowledge that to do so would be worse than taking the casualties. We sense that there would be, to use modern totem-pole wordage, a psychological, sociological rending of a thousand years' weaving. We would not only be defeated — we would be done.

As cities or as individuals, we will never encase ourselves in the thick lead suit of the Sunday supplements. The proof of this lies in these pages of Daniel Lang. He is a kind of modest Boswell to the special America that works and lives with the dividing atom, from the yellow outcropping on the New Mexico rock to the push-button that frequently blinds some spot of this earth with a quick touch of the sun. He shows us in detail how these Americans have adjusted their hopes and fears and daily habits at close range with the Thing. And so will the rest of us adjust as we come ourselves within range.

I can only suggest the factual wealth of this report on what one might call the human ecology of the atom, and poorly indicate what internal changes the report reveals in those human beings most intimately involved. I am a professional peruser of the daily news and much that I daily read and hear of science and defense and politics makes deeper sense to me, now that I have absorbed Mr. Lang's report. I can understand better the gulf that has happened between the older creative generation of nuclear physicists and the young generation of prestige-title-equipment-conscious scientists in this new era of "fashionable physics." I think I can understand better the impatience of government toward certain laboratory states of mind, and on the basis of the fortunate German failure, as told to Lang by Dr. Samuel Goudsmit, the reflective physicist's fear of government. It gives new meaning to the concept of positive security as against the current obsession with negative-police security.

If I may appropriately add this very personal note, the Lang conversations with such men as Drs. von Braun, Goudsmit, and Pollard also re-created for me an almost mystic experience of my youth. Once, half dozing through some lecture as a university freshman, I suddenly understood in a flash of intuition why man would never discover the secret of the universe and the origin of life. I knew this for certain, but in later years the certainty and the vision were obscured in the general clutter of my mind. I know now this was because of the waning of my *religious* instinct. Von Braun to Lang: ". . . the words that sound deep are really poorly contrived disguises for ignorance. Energy? Matter? We use them but we don't really know what they are." Man will never discover the ultimate secrets because though he lay them all bare before him, he can only label them, he cannot, ever, *understand* them.

I can believe von Braun and Pollard when they say, in the words of the former, "Any real scientist ends up a religious man."

Goudsmit with his chalk and his formulae is really no closer than Paddy Martinez with his cigarette and the yellow chunk in his saddle bag.

"Human imagination has its limits." This is our peril — and our safety. It is why, as Lang's report so clearly demonstrates, the strange society of the atom workers is no longer strange, the new era already old.

ERIC SEVAREID

May 1954
Washington, D.C.

CONTENTS

xi

The Man in the Thick Lead Suit

i

A ROMANTIC URGE

AMONG THE SPOILS of the Second World War that still belong to us — and to the Russians and the British and perhaps another victor or two — are some of the German scientists whose creative ingenuity accounted for so many Nazi military successes. Not long after the Allied armies crossed the German borders, their commanders, possibly more realistic than the millions back home who were cheering the arrival of what they thought would be a long peace, dispatched carefully chosen units to forage for this human booty. The roundup was not a joint operation. Each of the powers was out to acquire for itself, against the day when it might again be at war, the services of as many of these gifted enemy specialists as possible — airplane designers, guided-missile men, physicists, and the like. The American entry in the free-for-all was known as Operation Paperclip, and as a result of the efforts of its uniformed talent scouts, hundreds of strategically valuable German expatriates have been engaged in this country on projects for our Army, Navy, and Air Force, as well as for such large industrial companies as Bell Aircraft and General Electric. The Russians, of course, gave Operation Paperclip stiff competition, and succeeded in making off with a number of scientific catches, but our military leaders are of the opinion that the Paperclip agents got the better bag.

Whatever the score, a man who was one of the most sought-after prizes of this melancholy contest is now cerebrating for our Army within the borders of the United States. Not long ago, I had a talk with him, during which he discussed his career in Germany, his life in this country, and his thoughts about the future. The man is Professor Wernher von Braun, a scientist who served Hitler as head of the experimental guided-missile station at Peenemünde. It was at this seacoast town on the Baltic that von Braun, with five thousand men working under him, developed Germany's *Vergeltungswaffe Zwei* (Revenge Weapon Two), the famous V-2 that pounded London and Antwerp. The mounting of rocket engines on conventional Messerschmitt fighters was another innovation in which he had a hand. So was the *Wasserfall,* a guided anti-aircraft rocket that, after many successful test flights, was about to be turned loose against Allied planes just as the war ended. "I maintain that the *Wasserfall* is an effective way of defending cities like New York against air raids," von Braun told me. Only two months before Operation Paperclip brought about his transfer to his current sponsor, von Braun was poring over detailed plans for yet another revenge weapon — a transoceanic missile that could pound New York.

My interview with von Braun took place in his home near the reservation at Redstone Arsenal, just outside Huntsville, Alabama, where he is director of research-and-development projects at an Army Ordnance Guided Missile Center. The center used to be at Fort Bliss, near El Paso, but was shifted east when the Redstone reservation, a much larger area, was made available. Details of rocket developments at Redstone are, of course, secret, but there is nothing secret about the broad objective of all such centers, in this country and elsewhere. That objective is to build a guided missile capable of carrying an atomic warhead to any point on the face of the earth. As might be expected, von Braun is an important factor in whatever progress is being made at Redstone. The setup there is very much the same as the one he knew at Peenemünde: He is a civilian with a civilian staff, the core of which consists of a hundred and seventeen German scientists, engineers, and technicians who worked under him in the old days, and his immediate superior is an Army man. This man is Major James P. Hamill, the administrative officer in charge of the German contingent, a thirty-one-year-old physicist and Fordham graduate who speaks German. He was a member of Operation Paperclip and has known von Braun and the others since the day they entered American employ. Before meeting von Braun, I had a talk with Hamill in his office, where he told me something about the unusual command that came his way after the war. His security officer, Major Joseph Sestito, a large, cheerful man, was present.

Hamill's opening remark was automatic; he asked me not to discuss the Center's work with von Braun. "He wouldn't tell you anything anyway," Hamill said. "None of them would. They've been security-conscious a long, long time. After all, Peenemünde was Germany's Oak Ridge." Sestito observed that he thought the scientists' sense of protocol was every bit as strong as their security-consciousness. "In spite of all they've been through together, the non-Ph.D.s wouldn't dream of entering an automobile ahead of the Herr Doktors," he said. "The Herr Professors receive the same respect from the Herr Doktors. And all defer to von Braun, although he's only thirty-nine. He has an office of his own, by the way. Right above this one."

"He's among the youngest, in fact," Hamill said. "He and his brother, Magnus, who's a chemist here." He smiled as he continued, in a reminiscent mood, "You know, the instinctive dread these Germans have of ruffling a superior got me into a jam a couple of years ago, when an influential member of the Research and Development Board flew out from Washington to visit us at Fort Bliss. We were coming out of one of the buildings there when he said to me, 'I hope you're letting them feel they can discuss scientific matters in a free-and-easy way. We certainly don't want some young major putting them through infantry drill or anything like that.' 'Naturally not,' I said. Just then, a half-dozen Paperclip boys came along. When they saw me, they immediately flattened themselves against the building wall, whipped off their hats, and shouted in unison, 'Good morning, Major Hamill!' My visitor was charitable enough to change the subject."

The Germans, I learned from Hamill, started arriving in this country late in the summer of 1945. They came as "wards of the Army," and thus required no entry permits. Each of them voluntarily signed a one-year contract with the Army. Subsequently, new five-year contracts, subject to termination in three years at the Army's discretion, were drawn up, and these were signed by one and all. (They were later renewed.) "I can't disclose the men's salaries," Hamill said, "but they're modest compared to what they would earn in private industry." In 1947, the Peenemünde scientists at Fort Bliss were joined by three hundred more wards of the Army. These were the parents, wives, and children of the scientists, who up to that time had been cared for at a camp for Paperclip dependents in Landshut, Bavaria. Two of the new arrivals were von Braun's parents, the Baron and Baroness Magnus von Braun, whose ancestral estate in Silesia had been confiscated by the Russians. A third was his eighteen-year-old bride, a second cousin he had known all his life and to whom he proposed by mail; von Braun had been permitted to leave El Paso and go to Landshut to marry her and accompany her back to Fort Bliss.

The Germans, who at Fort Bliss were quartered in a former hospital annex, kept pretty much to themselves at first, but gradually, as some of them acquired automobiles, they began spending more and more time in El Paso, where they shopped, went to movies and night clubs, and became acquainted with the residents. "They learned English with a Texas twang," Hamill said. "They had sombreros and cowboy boots to go with it. Their children went to El Paso schools, where they generally received high grades from their teachers, and bloody noses from the American and Mexican kids, who thought the war was still on. Their parents never came to us about that, though. They just told their kids to take care of themselves." Unlike the children, the parents ran into hardly any antagonism in El Paso. What little there was came from a few G.I.s on the post, who made a point of telling the Germans they were lucky to be eating three squares. "Nowadays they'd complain about such treatment, but at the time they didn't let out a peep," Sestito said. "They seemed to have a group spirit, based on the idea that on each one's model behavior rested the glory of the Reich. Also, they may have figured they'd be sent back to Germany if they showed any resentment. An aerodynamics man who was telling me one day about an unfriendly G.I. wound up by saying, 'Maybe he lost someone in the war. I can understand.' "

As it happened, two of the Paperclip men *were* sent back to Germany, but not for showing resentment. One was incompetent. The other went off to Juárez on a lark. It was then a violation of an Army order to cross the short bridge over the Rio Grande that connects El Paso with the Mexican town. "The Germans were our wards," Hamill explained, "and we didn't want to risk any possible international incidents. Fortunately, this particular fellow wasn't much use to us and wouldn't be to the Russians, so I didn't hesitate to make an example of him." Sestito said that two years later, in 1948, the Army found itself in the position of requiring the scientists to cross the bridge. This was done at the insistence of the State Department, which complained that technically the Germans weren't in the United States at all. Von Braun and his colleagues, following instructions, therefore showed up at the American Consulate in Juárez, where they filled out visa forms. "Port of embarkation was given as Ciudad Juárez," Sestito said. "Port of arrival, El Paso. Method of travel, El Paso City Lines. That's a trolley line. The fare's four cents."

When the scientists and their families had their visas, they became resident aliens and, except for certain standard reservations, were on an equal footing with American citizens. The Army thereupon lifted some of the restrictions that had been placed on the Germans. Censoring of their mail ceased, although for months afterward the Germans insisted on showing their letters to Hamill or Sestito. Increasingly, classified information was made accessible to them, and they were no longer under surveillance when they traveled. (Previously, when it had been necessary for them to make trips to places like the General Electric plant, in Schenectady, agents of the Counter Intelligence Corps had checked their trains or planes at stops along the way to make sure they were still aboard.) Furthermore, the Germans were informed that when their contracts expired, they might, if they chose, quit working for the Army and enter private industry. On the face of it, Sestito told me, the scientists can even return to Germany upon the expiration of their contracts. "However," he added, "they possess knowledge of classified information, and so, I believe, there are certain legal provisions whereby their return could be prevented, if any of them *should* want to go back." Three other Germans besides von Braun have been back to their homeland on brief visits, one of them also to be married in Landshut and the others to receive long-overdue Ph.D. degrees at the University of Darmstadt. "Resident aliens or not," Sestito said to me, "they were restricted to Western Germany, and C.I.C. men kept tabs on them all the time. And they most certainly weren't allowed to go to Berlin. Why run the risk of Russian kidnappings?"

As resident aliens, the Germans were entitled to apply for American citizenship. All of them did, and now have their first papers, Hamill told me. "By the way," he added, "the group has been investigated thoroughly by both the Army and the F.B.I. You never know when someone's going to ask about that." In Hitler's day, Sestito said, about eighty per cent of the Redstone Germans were members of either the National Socialist Party or some other Nazi organization. "Von Braun himself joined the Nazi Party in 1940," he went on. "I'm fairly sure that these men became members more or less as a matter of expediency, rather than ideology. Not that I'm swearing they're one-hundred-per-cent sold on American institutions. In fact, any political attitude they may have toward their work seems to shape up as a neat syllogism out of some latter-day Goebbels: Germanic culture has always been the leader of Western culture; Western culture is now being championed by the United States against Russia's Eastern culture; therefore, the United States is the champion of Germanic culture. I believe they joined Nazi organizations primarily to hold on to their jobs. Their work is the driving force in their lives, not just a way of making a living. I'm glad they're working for us and not for some other country, and I hope they all keep renewing their contracts. They're good, very good." Hamill indicated several documents with red covers marked "SECRET." "We're making progress," he said. Then he looked up at the ceiling. "That guy upstairs wants to go to the moon," he said. "That's his passion — interplanetary travel. Whether it will be war or peace on earth comes after that for him."

Hamill told me that his assignment had been gratifying to him for personal as well as military reasons. He has derived deep satisfaction from watching the Germans gradually adjust themselves to their new environment. "They're eating hominy grits," Sestito put in. "Also enchilada sauce. That's the Mexican influence from El Paso. On the other hand, the Huntsville grocery stores are selling sauerkraut for the first time." I asked Hamill whether he thought von Braun and the rest would be able to readjust to their old environment if they ever found themselves back in Germany. "I'm not sure," he said slowly. "The kids they brought with them were three to eighteen when they came over. Already, two of the eighteen-year-olds have married Americans — Texans, incidentally. Thirty children have been born here. Children are anchors, you know. No, I'm not at all sure. These people have become used to things. It might be too much of an effort for them to migrate again. I don't mean as scientists — they could be that anywhere. I mean as human beings."

At Hamill's request, Sestito led me up a flight of stairs to von Braun's office, a large room containing a conference table as well as a desk. As we entered, von Braun rose from the desk and strode buoyantly toward us. He is a startlingly handsome man, over six feet tall, blue-eyed, blond, athletic-looking. His expression struck me as exuberant rather than reflective, and his manner as that of a man accustomed to being regarded as indispensable. He shook my hand energetically. "I will pick you up at your hotel after dinner and drive you to my house, where we will talk," he said. He laughed heartily and continued, "Germany is three countries. The Rhineland is the wine country. Bavaria is the beer country. Prussia and Silesia are the land of schnapps. I am from Silesia, so tonight you and I will have schnapps together."

Von Braun and I arrived at his home, a small two-story frame house, shortly after eight o'clock. His wife, an extremely pretty young woman, met us at the door and anxiously asked my indulgence for the appearance of the place. "We're moving in a few days," she explained. "We're in the middle of packing."

"We've just had a new house built," her husband said. "Much more room in it than here. Especially for my daughter. She's two. We're going to have three bedrooms, a terrace, and a porch. And a white shingle exterior. The house is on top of a hill, so we'll have a view, too. Huntsville, with its green and mountains, reminds me of Silesia. I found El Paso sandy and dry."

Actually, the von Braun living room, in which I spent the evening, showed only minor signs of decamping. Three packing cases crammed with furnishings stood off to one side, and the light was dim because, Mrs. von Braun said, a couple of lamps had already been removed to the new house. Apart from that, all appeared to be in order. Von Braun and I seated ourselves on two comfortable facing sofas beneath a dark Rembrandt reproduction that gazed down on us from the wall. Between us, on a low table, rested an Americanized version of Silesian hospitality — bourbon and soda. Mrs. von Braun brought in a tray of small sandwiches and cakes from the kitchen and then excused herself, saying that she must go upstairs and continue her packing.

Von Braun started off by telling me that his childhood had been spent in first one German city and then another, depending on where his father, who worked for the Ministry of Agriculture, happened to be stationed. His absorption with rockets began in 1930, when he was eighteen and was just embarking on the studies that eventually led to a Ph.D. in physics at the University of Berlin. Specifically, it was an article in a magazine devoted to astronomy that inspired his fervor. "I don't remember the name of the magazine or the author, but the article described an imaginary trip to the moon," he said. "It filled me with a romantic urge. Interplanetary travel! Here was a task worth dedicating one's life to! Not just to stare through a telescope at the moon and the planets but to soar through the heavens and actually explore the mysterious universe! I knew how Columbus had felt." Von Braun's romantic urge led him to consort with some talented but impecunious rocket enthusiasts who had banded together to form an organization called the *Verein für Raumschiffahrt* (Spaceship Travel Club) and were using an abandoned three-hundred-acre arsenal, which they called their *Raketenflugplatz* (Rocket Flight Place), on the outskirts of Berlin, as a proving ground for some rudimentary missiles they had built. The members of the club, many of whom later figured prominently in the doings at Peenemünde, had wangled a free lease on the dump from the municipal authorities and went about scrounging materials from manufacturers by talking fast about the rosy future of rocket travel. They recruited free manpower by letting unemployed mechanics live in the concrete igloos and warehouses that dotted the area. In spite of their penury, the members steadily improved their rockets, and word of their accomplishments began to get around.

One day in the spring of 1932, a black sedan drew up at the edge of the *Raketenflugplatz* and three passengers got out to watch a rocket launching. "They were in mufti, but mufti or not, it was the Army," von Braun said to me. "That was the beginning. The Versailles Treaty hadn't placed any restrictions on rockets, and the Army was desperate to get back on its feet. We didn't care much about that, one way or the other, but we needed money, and the Army seemed willing to help us. In 1932, the idea of war seemed to us an absurdity. The Nazis weren't yet in power. We felt no moral scruples about the possible future abuse of our brain child. We were interested solely in exploring outer space. It was simply a question with us of how the golden cow would be milked most successfully." After the appearance of the black sedan, the golden cow supplied the members of the *Verein für Raumschiffahrt* generously with equipment, proving grounds, and skilled workmen. Von Braun, I gathered, was singled out by the Army as the group's boy wonder. He spent the Christmas of 1935 at his father's estate in Silesia, and while there he mentioned that he was scouting for a coastal site that could be used as an experimental station. "Why don't you look at Peenemünde?" his mother asked. "Your grandfather used to go duck-shooting there." Von Braun did so. "It was love at first sight," he told me. "Marvelous sailing."

Hitler, upon coming into power, poured twenty million marks into Peenemünde and speeded its construction by granting it priorities on material and labor. By 1937, the station was completed, and von Braun, now attached as a civilian to the German Army's Ordnance Department, took over as technical director. His titular superior was Major General Walter Dornberger, a physicist himself, with a Ph.D. from the University of Berlin, who had long been interested in rockets and who had been one of the three passengers in the black sedan. (General Dornberger, another Paperclip find, is currently with the Bell Aircraft Company.) From the outset, the experiments were aimed at developing the V-2. "Many fanciful stories have described the V-2 as part of a devilish plan devised by Hitler for use against the city of London," von Braun said. "The real story is much less sinister and dramatic. One day, a year before Peenemünde opened, Dornberger said to me, 'The Ordnance Department expects us to make a field weapon capable of carrying a large warhead over a range much beyond that of artillery. We can't hope to stay in business if we keep on firing only experimental rockets.' "

Bounding up from his sofa, von Braun went to a table and came back with an album of snapshots taken over the years at Peenemünde. Turning its pages, I saw pictures of him in a blockhouse, at test stands, and in a deep-sea diver's costume, about to plunge into the Baltic to retrieve the parts of a missile that had landed in the sea. One picture was of a banquet given at Peenemünde in von Braun's honor. "That was taken in 1944," he said. "I'd just received the Knight's Cross for the V-2. I was also given the honorary degree of Research Professor by Hitler. That's why I'm called Professor today. A very high award — Willy Messerschmitt [inventor of the fighter plane named after him] was given one, too. Not many people knew about it, because our work was always kept so secret. It's odd, but I'm better known in your country than I was in my own."

Putting the album aside and returning to the story of Peenemünde, von Braun said that after the Nazis marched against Poland, the Luftwaffe became Hitler's great pet and his interest in guided missiles lagged. Peenemünde's priorities dropped lower and lower. Technicians there were refused military deferments and were converted into infantrymen. Early in the summer of 1942, Dornberger and von Braun visited Hitler at his headquarters in East Prussia. They tried to persuade him that, in view of the way the Luftwaffe was flagging, guided missiles were Germany's one sound offensive bet. "No luck," von Braun told me. "The next day, we received word that *der Führer* had dreamed during the night that our rockets would not work." On October 3, 1942, von Braun said, a launching, or, as he called it, a shoot, at Peenemünde was so successful that Dornberger was moved to exclaim, "This afternoon the spaceship was born!" Further encouraging shoots took place, and in July 1943 the General and von Braun made a second pilgrimage to East Prussia. *"Der Führer* looked much older, and he was wearing his first pair of glasses," von Braun recalled. "But when we described our accomplishments to him, his face lighted with enthusiasm. He revoked his dream."

Hitler's enthusiasm was almost as trying as his indifference had been. Peenemünde became overrun with officials wanting to know how fast mass production of the V-2s could get under way. Von Braun protested that his rockets were still in the experimental stage, but Hitler's lieutenants couldn't wait. By February 1944 the Baltic station was so firmly entrenched as Hitler's pet that Heinrich Himmler, the chief of the Gestapo, approached von Braun with a proposal that it be transferred to S.S. sponsorship. "He assured me that Hitler's door was always open to him," von Braun said, "and that with him I would not be bothered by the red tape that the Army always put in the way of gifted inventors." Von Braun informed Himmler that he admired General Dornberger and that mass production was being held up by technical problems, not red tape. Apparently, Himmler was miffed, for three weeks later von Braun was awakened at two in the morning by three Gestapo agents, taken to Stettin, and put in a prison. He was held there for two weeks. During this time, a court of inquiry asked him to disprove a charge that he had been planning to fly to England with secret documents in a small plane the Army had placed at his disposal. Von Braun could only deny the charge. "One day while the inquiry was in full swing, Dornberger burst into the room and presented some papers that brought about my immediate release," he told me. "Dornberger had gone directly to Hitler's headquarters about my predicament."

Despite various ups and downs, von Braun continued, the V-2's accuracy was improved (how, he did not say, and I did not ask), hundreds of soldiers were trained in the firing of rockets, and a vast subterranean production plant was set up at Nordhausen, two hundred miles southwest of Peenemünde, in the heart of Germany. On September 7, 1944, the first V-2 was fired at London. "The Allies had bombed us several times at Peenemünde," von Braun said, "but we felt a genuine regret that our missile, born of idealism, like the airplane, had joined in the business of killing. We had designed it to blaze the trail to other planets, not to destroy our own." Then, almost harshly, he said, "But it was too late for the V-2 to stem the tide. We needed another year. *Der Führer* didn't seem to realize how immature our weapon still was." Von Braun shrugged, and added, "If Germany had won the war, *der Führer* would probably have lost interest in rockets. His enthusiasm would have shifted to a huge reconstruction project in the Ukraine or some such. I just know it."

After a moment's silence, von Braun unexpectedly let out a jolly laugh. "The amusing thing about my country's collapse was that the V-2 crowd had its choice of what to do," he said. "The High Command and the Ministry of Armament wanted us to move west. The Army corps commander defending Pomerania wanted us to stay and help him. In the end, we decided for ourselves. That was at the beginning of 1945. The Russians were only a hundred miles away, and we could already see that an Iron Curtain was coming down. General Dornberger and I wanted our outfit to fall into American hands." I asked why, and von Braun smiled. "My country had lost two wars in my young lifetime," he replied. "The next time, I wanted to be on the winning side." Not everyone at Peenemünde shared von Braun's views, with the result that when, during January and February, he and some four hundred of his most skilled colleagues headed for the so-called Bavarian Redoubt to hide out from the S.S. until the end of the war, a good many others stayed behind to await the arrival of the Russians. Thanks to Peenemünde's restored high priority rating, the railroads provided transportation for von Braun and his party, and the Navy agreed to ship twelve thousand tons of his technical equipment to Lübeck, where it was to be loaded on barges and sent up the Elbe to Magdeburg, and then moved by train from there to the Redoubt. Seventy per cent of this equipment, stranded on the docks at Lübeck and Magdeburg, was eventually grabbed by the Russians.

The guided-missile people, scattered throughout twenty-five closely bunched but isolated Bavarian villages, settled down to await capture. The waiting lasted from early April until the middle of May. "There I was, living royally in a ski hotel on a mountain plateau," von Braun said. "There were the French below us to the west, and the Americans to the south. But no one, of course, suspected we were there. So nothing happened. The most momentuous events were being broadcast over the radio. Hitler was dead, the war was over, an armistice was signed — and the hotel service was excellent." Finally, on May 10th, von Braun grew tired of waiting and sent his brother Magnus down the mountain on a bicycle in search of the American Army. With the help of a G.I. he came across at the foot of the mountain, Magnus made his way to a Counter Intelligence Corps headquarters in the small Austrian town of Reutte, where he informed the officer in charge that the top V-2 men were only a couple of miles away. The officer, who had not yet been briefed on Paperclip objectives, told Magnus to come back the following day and bring his colleagues. The next morning, the party drove down the mountain in a fleet of cars. "Did you think you might be arrested and punished?" I asked von Braun. "Why, no," he replied in a tone of surprise. "We wouldn't have treated your atomic scientists as war criminals, and I didn't expect to be treated as one. No, I wasn't afraid. It all made sense. The V-2 was something we had and you didn't have. Naturally, you wanted to know all about it." He laughed, and added, "When we reached the C.I.C., I wasn't kicked in the teeth or anything. They immediately fried us some eggs."

From Reutte, von Braun and his associates were taken to Garmisch-Partenkirchen, where a Paperclip interrogation camp for German scientists had been set up. Here, he told me, he was questioned by Dr. Richard Porter, of General Electric, and Dr. Fritz Zwicky and Dr. Clark Millikan, of the California Institute of Technology. "Their questioning, of course, was extremely intelligent," von Braun said. "Those men are top scientists. I still do business with them." British scientists were eager to talk with him, and in August he was flown to London. He spent two weeks there. He and some other German rocket experts were billeted at an Army camp near Wimbledon, where they were picked up daily by an Air Force Intelligence officer and driven to the Ministry of Supply. "I must admit that I thought the British might be unfriendly to me," von Braun said, "but I found I was wrong the first day I spent at the Ministry. I was interviewed there by Sir Alwyn Douglas Crow, the man in charge of developing British rockets. I was hardly inside his office before we were engaged in friendly shoptalk. He was curious about the headaches we'd had at Peenemünde, and he gave me a good picture of the damage the V-2 had done in England. He told me that in June 1944 the British had learned the details of what we were up to at Peenemünde by piecing together the debris of one of our test rockets that had accidentally landed in Sweden. I must say they made an excellent analysis."

In the course of his commuting between Wimbledon and the Ministry, von Braun, who had got to know London fairly well while on a pleasure trip there in 1934, during his student days, had a chance to observe some of the damage that had been wrought on the British capital. At first, he said, he was amazed by how much less rubble there was in London than in Berlin, but then he realized that it was because Berlin, having taken its worst punishment at the very end of the war, hadn't yet had time to clean up its debris. "One day, the Air Force officer driving me in to London stopped our car in front of the remains of a downtown building that had been struck by a V-2," he said. "It looked as if it had been a six-story office building, but I was unable to tell the precise way in which the V-2 had done its damage, because the rubble had been cleared away. The officer started up the car again after a few minutes, and, for some reason, I found myself wondering as we drove off where our German agents in London had disappeared to. I never did find out, but one thing I know is that we had some good ones there. Our battery commanders on the French coast used to have reports on V-2 effectiveness within an hour after a rocket had been launched. I've never heard in so many words how the reports reached them, but I assume it was by radio."

Early in September, von Braun and four other German scientists were flown from London to Fort Strong, near Boston. They were the first of the Peenemünde group to reach this country. Von Braun's companions were sent on to the Aberdeen Proving Ground, in Maryland, to help our scientists there fathom the contents of documents concerning German rockets that had come into our possession. Von Braun was met at Fort Strong by Major Hamill and driven to Washington, where he had several long conversa-

tions with Army Ordnance officers in the Pentagon. He and Hamill
then left by train for the West, where von Braun, as his first American assignment, joined some other Germans in teaching military
personnel how to launch captured V-2s at the Army's White Sands
Proving Ground, the New Mexican desert outpost eighty miles
from El Paso. "That job took eight months," von Braun said.
"We seemed to be expected to do it in two weeks, but shooting
a V-2 is a complicated and dangerous business. Especially the
rusty, dried-out V-2s we had at White Sands. And the facilities
there were unsuitable for efficient shoots. Frankly, we were dis-
appointed with what we found in this country during our first
year or so. At Peenemünde, we'd been coddled. Here you were
counting pennies. Your armed forces were being demobilized and
everybody wanted military expenditures curtailed. Of course, our
facilities are more adequate now. The situation has improved."

I asked von Braun if the working conditions he had found here
had caused him to regret not having signed on with the Russians.
"No," he replied, "but working in a dictatorship can have its
advantages, if the regime is behind you. I'm convinced that the
man in charge of Stalin's atom bomb just has to press a button
and he'll be supplied with a whole concentration camp full of
labor. We used to have thousands of Russian prisoners of war
working for us at Peenemünde. But I'm also convinced that living conditions in Russia can't compare with America's. The Russians are probably paying the scientists they got from Peenemünde
well, but a refrigerator or an automobile just isn't there to be
bought. I recently read in a German newspaper that some of
my former colleagues at Peenemünde are living near Moscow in
crowded prefabricated log cabins sent by Finland as reparations.
I often get to thinking about the scientists I knew in Germany who
I presume are in Russia now. There was Gröttrop, for one — an
excellent electronics and guidance-control man. And Putzer, a
first-rate production man, who managed the Linke-Hofmann

heavy-machinery plant in Breslau. And Schierhorn, who knows everything about aluminum welding. I wish I had them and some of the others here with me, but I do think the United States got the best of our group. The Americans looked for brains, the Russians for hands. The Russians have a great many production engineers who can make wonderful copies of V-2s. The American approach has been to see the whole business as a field for development, to try for something better than anything made at Peenemünde."

Von Braun shook his head. "I can't understand about Gröttrop," he said. "He was the only one of the inner circle at Peenemünde who deliberately went over to the Russians. He may have thought they would make him the key man in their guided-missile projects. Perhaps they have, but Gröttrop was the kind who talked back if he didn't like something — he didn't care who it was. He believed in his personal freedom. I think he made a mistake in choosing Russia."

Once the White Sands teaching chore was out of the way, von Braun settled down to research at Fort Bliss. At first, most of his off hours were also spent there. He told me that when he did go in to El Paso, he encountered practically no hostility. "Some D.P.s in El Paso who learned who I was treated me distantly," he said, "but there were also some D.P.s, with an interest in history, who came and looked me up. Apparently, what had gone on in the Third Reich was still a mystery to them, and they thought I could explain it to them." In the spring of 1947, von Braun went to Germany for his wedding. "I had a feeling of narrowness there," he said. "In Europe, one is always crossing borders, but here one can travel thousands of miles without a passport." The arrival of his bride and of his parents made the United States seem less strange to him as a new home, and being married gave him a more active social life. It also made him aware that his quarters at Fort Bliss weren't ample enough. "Even this house we're leaving now would have seemed like a mansion in Texas," he told me. Late in 1948, the von Brauns' daughter was born, and their house became even less adequate. "My daughter is beautiful," von Braun said. "Perhaps you will see her. My wife picks her up at ten each night for a few minutes."

As his domestic and social interests broadened, von Braun said, so did his professional life. The laboratories at Fort Bliss and the scope of the research projects there were enlarged. He was pleased, too, with a variety of new equipment that was installed at White Sands. "Shoots are the climaxes in my field," he said. "A first-rate proving ground is essential. You put six months of work into a missile and inside of a minute it's either a failure or a success." In 1948, the Army gave von Braun permission to attend scientific conventions. At one of these, in Chicago, assembled by the Air Force Surgeon General to consider medical problems associated with interplanetary travel, von Braun read a paper on man-made satellites. "Everyone has been most friendly to me at meetings," he said. "Science is as much a universal language as music." In August 1949 the British Interplanetary Society invited von Braun to become an honorary fellow, "in recognition of your great pioneering activities in the field of rocket engineering." In accepting, von Braun replied, in part, "Despite the grief the work of me and my associates brought to the British people, [your invitation] is the most encouraging proof that the noble enthusiasm in the future of rocketry is stronger than national sentiments."

The headlights of an automobile coming out of a driveway across the street shone brilliantly into von Braun's living room, lighting up the gloomy Rembrandt and the packing boxes. When the car had gone and the room was somber again, von Braun told me that the shift to Alabama, in 1950, had seemed no wrench at all. By then, he said, he and his wife had become used to thinking of the United States as their home. "We were no longer surprised when people called each other by their first names a few minutes after being introduced," he went on. "And when we saw a supermarket here in Huntsville, we knew we were all set. Everything in one store! In Germany, even vegetable shops are specialized." Soon, von Braun told me, he and his family would be enjoying the view from their new house. As for his parents, they have a comfortable home near by. "They are our sitters," he said.

Certainly, von Braun assured me, the move to Alabama hadn't interfered in the slightest with his research. "I can work anywhere in the world," he said. "I've finished 'Mars Project' since coming here. That's my novel. I worked on it for three years. It deals with a trip to Mars by seventy passengers aboard ten spaceships. The first half describes preparations for the flight and the second tells about settling on Mars. That second part shows what scientific developments will be able to do if our civilization succeeds in surviving a few more years. My characters live underground in pressurized, air-conditioned homes, and all their food is synthesized. In the end, Mars and Earth work out their scientific problems through mutual aid."

"But what about the moon?" I asked.

"Mars is more of a challenge," von Braun replied. "It would take two hundred and sixty days to get there. To the moon it's only a hundred hours." He hesitated momentarily. Then he spoke with an intensity he had not shown all evening. "Personally, though, I'd rather go to the moon than to Mars, even if the trip is shorter," he said. "After all, a journey to the Moon is unquestionably a possibility. The moon's face, thanks to telescopes, is more familiar to us than even some parts of the earth — the mountain ranges in Tibet, for example. All that's needed is adequate funds and continuity of effort. Spaceships will eventually be used by everybody. All this military application of rockets — it's only a part of the picture. A means to an end."

I asked von Braun if he had ever regretted the arrival of the black sedan two decades ago at the *Raketenflugplatz*. He shook his head. "Someone else would have done the job if I hadn't," he said. "Rockets were a new idea, and a new idea is stronger than one man's feelings. Once civilization is committed to technical advance, we have to keep going. We can't go back to a pastoral existence. That would destroy the social bases of our modern life. Think of the men in industry who would be thrown out of work. Think of the way populations are increasing — those people couldn't be fed. The main question is how we use our technical advances. They can either kill us or elevate us. In ancient Greece, slaves did the dishwashing while Sophocles wrote his tragedies. Literally, we don't have slavery today, but the bulk of humanity is in bondage to physical chores. Technology offers millions a chance to investigate the higher aspects of life. But you don't get something for nothing. There are strings attached to that chance." Von Braun paused, and then continued, "The same things would have happened at Peenemünde without me. Do you think scientists should be blamed for wars? Einstein? He looked for fundamental truths and his formula was used for an atomic bomb. Alexander Graham Bell? Military orders that kill thousands are transmitted over his telephone. Why not blame the bus driver who takes war workers to their factories? How about movie actors who sing for the troops?"

"Have you any answer for it all?" I asked.

"Religion," von Braun replied at once. "As long as national sovereignties exist, our only hope is to raise everybody's standards of ethics. I go to church regularly now."

"Did you at Peenemünde?"

"I went occasionally," he said. "But it's really too late to go to church after a war starts. One becomes very busy." He waved his hand vaguely. "Any real scientist ends up a religious man. The more he learns about natural science, the more he sees that the words that sound deep are really poorly contrived disguises for ignorance. Energy? Matter? We use them but we don't really know what they are. Or take the mystery of heredity. It will never be solved." He laughed. "None of us have anything to do with the most fateful event in our lives — picking our parents."

Right now, von Braun said, world conditions being what they are, he can't see himself doing anything other than continuing at Redstone. He regards his present course as essentially the one he followed at Peenemünde. "Still developing military rockets. And still hoping for spaceships," he said. "Only now I'm doing it in a different country. But soon it won't even seem like a different country. I used to spend my week ends sailing on the Baltic. Now I fish in T.V.A. lakes. Sometimes, at Redstone, soldiers in training for technical jobs have to mop our laboratory floors. They gripe about it the same way the soldiers did at Peenemünde. Gröttrop is probably listening to the same gripes in Russia."

We heard Mrs. von Braun coming down the stairs. "Wernher!" she called out softly as she stepped from the landing. Their daughter, half asleep, was in her arms. Von Braun and I stood up, and he walked toward his wife. She glanced at me to see if I was admiring the baby. I was indeed. She is a beautiful child — blond, curly-headed, lanky for her age. The living-room lights gradually roused her. She blinked several times, and then her blue, still-sleepy eyes opened wide. She caught sight of her father and drowsily reached out a hand toward him. He touched her fingers, bent down, and kissed her.

Von Braun and I didn't sit down again after his wife and daughter left. The interview was over. "I'm going to do some work at home tonight, and I have to be in at Redstone very early in the morning," he told me jauntily. "I leave for a shoot at White Sands in a few days."

SOMETHING IN THE SKY

ONE TYPE OF AERIAL DEVELOPMENT, guided or unguided, planetary or interplanetary, whichever it may be, that von Braun has so far not busied himself with is the flying saucer. That continuing mystery is one that the Air Force has been pondering since midsummer of 1947. It was then — at a time when the Air Force was already concerned with such problems as the refinement of supersonic craft, the rigging up of radar networks, and its budgetary skirmishing with the Army and Navy — that it found itself confronted by this new and completely different headache. People in every section of the country were seeing strange objects that streaked across the sky at tremendous speeds, and although these people, who included such practiced students of the heavens as airplane pilots, farmers, and the Lieutenant Governor of Idaho, were not able to identify the things they had seen, they were able to describe them vividly and unforgettably. The newspapers called the first of these puzzling objects a flying saucer, taking their cue from the man who reported having seen it and who described it as saucerlike, and the name stuck, although later people reported seeing things that looked like flying chromium hubcaps, flying dimes, flying teardrops, flying gaslights, flying ice-cream cones, and flying pie plates. As more and more curious things were seen in the skies, cautiously quizzical editorials began to appear in the papers, and the President and members of Congress received a deluge of letters demanding an explanation. Many of the letter writers had concluded that the objects, whatever they might be, were manned by Russians, and that as soon as their pilots had reconnoitered sufficiently, they would return loaded with atomic bombs. Others thought the earth was being visited by space ships from another planet. Still others suspected that our own Air Force was secretly testing some new form of aircraft. Everyone agreed, however, that it was up to the Air Force, as the custodian of our welkin, to explain the flying objects and, if necessary, to repel them. The result was the launching by the Air Force, on January 22, 1948, of a special investigation — an investigation that, though it has reached numerous conclusions, is still under way and has yet to put the public mind at rest.

It appears that, aside from the hope of reassuring a jittery populace, the Air Force, in embarking upon this undertaking, had any or all of three things in mind. It may well have shared the civilian concern over what, if anything, the Russians might have to do with the reported phenomena, and it may even have felt that to insure a thoroughgoing investigation there was certainly no harm in assuming for the moment that the era of interplanetary travel had arrived and the earth had become an objective for journeys from elsewhere in the solar system. Or — and this would not necessarily exclude the first two considerations — the Air Force may have been setting up a smoke screen to protect, in the interest of national security, the secret of some experimental flying objects of its own that only a trusted few of its members knew about. Whatever the purpose, the investigation, with which I have been in touch from time to time, has seemingly been exhaustive. The Air Force personnel originally assigned to it was later augmented by astronomers, psychologists, physicists, meteorologists, physicians, and representatives of the F.B.I. The investigation, which soon became popularly known as Project Saucer, was first headed by Lieutenant General Benjamin W. Chidlaw, Commanding General of the Air Matériel Command, and its base was, and is, at Wright Field, Dayton, Ohio. The project's task turned out to involve a mixture of old-fashioned detection, scientific analysis, public relations, and the study of a widespread state of mind. In December 1949, after checking, over a period of two years, three hundred and seventy-five reports of intruders in the sky, the Air Force publicly called it quits, but Project Saucer was not actually disbanded. National security, the Air Force announced at the time, was not endangered. The flying saucers were apparitions, it said, all attributable either to a failure to recognize conventional objects, to hoaxes, or to a mild form of mass hysteria. The Air Force, however, did not let the matter rest there.

Not long after the apparent demise of Project Saucer, I had a talk in Washington with Brigadier General Ernest Moore, then chief of Air Force Intelligence, in the course of which he made four categorical statements that I felt sure he had made many times before. "First off," he said, "the Russians have nothing to do with these so-called saucers; I'll swear to that on a stack of Bibles, if you like. Second, we don't have any secret new types of aircraft that could have started all this commotion. Third, nobody, in our opinion, has spotted space ships from some other planet. Fourth, everything our investigators learned has been made available to the public."

The first saucer incident occurred on the afternoon of June 24, 1947, when Kenneth Arnold, on a business trip for a Boise, Idaho, firm that makes fire-control equipment, was flying his private plane from Chehalis, Washington, to Yakima, Washington. The reflection of a bright flash on one wing caught his eye. He turned and, at a distance he thought was about twenty miles, saw what he took to be nine tailless aircraft heading toward Mount Rainier. "I could see their outlines quite plainly against the snow," Air Force Intelligence quoted him as saying. "They flew very close to the mountaintops, directly south to southeast, down the hog's-back of the range, flying like geese, in a diagonal, chainlike line, as if they were linked together . . . a chain of saucerlike things at least five miles long, swerving in and out of the high mountain peaks. They were flat . . . and so shiny that they reflected the sun like a mirror." Arnold said he watched the saucers for three minutes and estimated their speed at about twelve hundred miles an hour.

Air Force technicians, consulted by newspapermen, said that any object moving that fast would be invisible to the naked eye at Arnold's estimated distance. The press scoffed at Arnold's story, and he was resentful. "Even if I see a ten-story building flying through the air, I won't say a word about it," he declared, and when he got back to Boise he wrote a series of articles about his experience for a magazine called *Fate*.

No sooner were the skeptical newspaper accounts printed than dozens of people turned up with similar reports. Another resident of Boise spotted a disk over that city, "a half circle in shape, clinging to a cloud and just as bright and silvery-looking as a mirror caught in the rays of the sun." Lieutenant Governor Donald S. Whitehead, of Idaho, disclosed that one evening he had seen a comet-shaped object sailing over the western part of the state. It finally dipped below the horizon, he said. (Later on, the personnel of Project Saucer decided that the Lieutenant Governor had been looking at either Saturn or Mercury.) Four cops in Portland, Oregon, saw a group of disks "wobbling, disappearing, and reappearing."

Reports of other phenomena having been seen in the skies appeared in the papers almost daily. Two Army officers at Fort

Richardson, Alaska, reported seeing a spherical object flying through the air at incredible speed and leaving no vapor trail; some fishermen off Newfoundland saw a series of aerial flashes, silver to reddish in color; a lady in Oregon watched a group of saucers spell out "P-E-P-S-I," and alerted her neighbors to the presence of foreign agents practicing a secret code in our skies; an Oklahoma City man saw a saucer "the bulk of six B-29s"; and a prospector in the Cascade Mountains of Oregon saw six saucers in a group, banking in the sun — "round, silent, and not flying in formation." On the Fourth of July, 1947, there were twelve reports of saucers in widely separated parts of the United States. One of these saucers, sighted at Trenton, New Jersey, was traced to a fireworks display. Dr. Paul Fitts, an Ohio State University psychologist who was for a time attached to Project Saucer, considered this crowded condition in the holiday skies the result of mass suggestibility, the same jumpy trait that caused Americans to see Zeppelins overhead during and after the First World War. "Our graphs show that saucer incidents always increase dramatically after publicity," he has since told me. "The sky, you know, has been a source of exciting visions from time immemorial, and its attraction is particularly strong in our jittery moments."

From the beginning, the officers in charge of Project Saucer recognized a peculiar difficulty in their assignment. "If you look out the window and see something, how can I prove or disprove what it was if I didn't see it and you can't tell me much about what you saw?" Major Jerre Boggs, who was then the chief liaison officer between Wright Field and the high command in Washington, asked me one day shortly after Project Saucer had presumably become a thing of the past. "It would be different if flying saucers were known to exist. Then we could have collected evidence indicating the degrees of probability that such things were sighted and the reason for their appearance at a given place. But

it is impossible to prove, logically and with finality, a double negative — that is, that there are no flying saucers and that people
have not seen flying saucers. The best we could do under the circumstances was to deduce, first, from the fact that it had not been
proved, that saucers *had* been seen and, second, from the fact that
reasonable theories could be advanced to explain away all the
reports of seeing them, that probably nobody had seen them at all.
The fewer the theoretical explanations and the less plausible they
were, the more reason there was for suspecting people *had* seen
saucers." The Major shook his head, and continued, "It's a difficult
concept to grasp, but so was the job we were tackling."

I asked Major Boggs whether there was any way to account for
the epidemic of reports of strange celestial objects. "Of course
there is," he replied. "If you look up at the sky long enough, you
can almost always make out something there that appears strange.
And more people are looking up now than ever before. Kids don't
count freight cars any more; they count airplanes. People who
were trained in air observation during the war have gone right on
observing. Also, the public hasn't forgotten that the atomic bomb
was kept secret from it for three years. This time, people want to
know what's cooking, so they look up." Major Boggs sighed. "Time
was when people used to make a wish if they saw a shooting star.
Now they telephone the Air Force."

Major Boggs and I pondered this unromantic age in silence for
a moment. Then he returned briskly to the problems that had confronted the investigators. "The one tangible thing we had to work
on was the fact that the sky is full of things," he said. "I can't even
come close to estimating the number of commercial and military
aircraft up there at any given moment. Then, there are more than
five hundred outfits of one kind or another that release balloons
from time to time. These range from simple weather balloons, no
larger than a volleyball, to complicated clusters of balloons, as
big as a house, for radar soundings or cosmic-ray research. At

night, balloons always have trailing lights. In addition to all those balloons, there are advertising blimps, the sweeping beams of searchlights and air-lane beacons, clouds that reflect the sun and other sources of light, clouds scudding by the moon, and pieces of paper that are swirled aloft from the street by the wind. And, of course, birds, kites, St. Elmo's fire, meteors, comets, lightning, and fireballs — or, if you prefer, bolides, which are bits of interplanetary matter, with trajectories that sometimes seem to parallel the surface of the earth, trail a wisp of flame, and disintegrate with a flash when they hit the earth's dense atmosphere."

The officers in command of Project Saucer began by breaking this aerial hodgepodge down into its principal divisions, Major Boggs told me. Then they started looking for clues to what people had actually seen when they thought they were seeing flying saucers. Dr. J. Allen Hynek, the head of the Emerson McMillin Observatory, at Ohio State University, was called in to consider objects that might be of astral origin. The United States Weather Bureau, the Air Weather Service, and various other scientific set-ups, among them the Electronics Laboratory of the Cambridge Field Station, at Cambridge, Massachusetts, were asked to study the reports of sightings to determine whether any of their balloons were responsible. Airline schedules and flight charts of military aircraft were studied. In this work, Project Saucer had the assistance of the personnel attached to the Air Matériel Command laboratories at Wright Field. These included specialists in aerodynamics and propulsion — men who might be able to ascertain whether what were described as the maneuverings of a saucer might not really be the movements of an airplane or balloon. Wright Field physicians who had had experience with the limitations and idiosyncrasies of human beings in the air were also available for consultation, as were all kinds of engineers, in case any material evidence turned up. All told, at one time or another, some two hundred people were engaged on Project Saucer. It was agreed among them that they would not pool their ideas. "We didn't want them influencing each other," one officer explained to me. "We had enough suggestibility on our hands as it was."

Practical jokers, precocious children, publicity seekers, and mentally unbalanced people were among those who saw saucers, or said they did, but those who reported seeing them also included men whose reliability was such that if they had claimed to have seen flying gorillas, Project Saucer would have taken them seriously. Two of these were Captain C. S. Chiles and Pilot John B. Whitted, experienced Eastern Air Lines pilots. At 3 a.m. on July 24, 1948, these men, flying a passenger plane at five thousand feet near Montgomery, Alabama, saw something that the newspapers later called a "space ship." Chiles and Whitted didn't call it that. They said it was a "wingless aircraft," a hundred feet long, cigar-shaped, with a diameter about twice that of the fuselage of a B-29, and was moving a third faster than a jet plane. It seemed to have a row of windows above a globular cabin that suggested a pilot's compartment. The interior of the cabin was extraordinarily bright — as bright as a magnesium flare — and along its sides was a less brilliant glow, which looked like "a blue fluorescent factory light." The exhaust of the object seemed to be an orange-red flame. "We saw no occupants," Chiles said. "We saw it at the same time and asked each other, 'What in the world is this?' Whatever it was, it flashed down toward us and we veered to the left. It veered to its left and passed us about seven hundred feet to our right, and above us. Then, as if the pilot had seen us and wanted to avoid us, it pulled up with a tremendous burst of flame from the rear and zoomed into the clouds, its prop wash or jet wash rocking our DC-3." The only passenger in the plane who was not asleep at the time said he had seen the same thing the two pilots saw.

An hour before the two pilots and the wakeful passenger saw whatever they saw, ground observers at the Robins Air Force

Base, at Macon, Georgia, nearly two hundred miles to the northeast, also saw something peculiar in the sky. They reported that
it had been flying faster than a jet plane, that it had trailed vari-
colored flames, that it was heading toward Montgomery, and that
it had behaved like a normal aircraft in the way it disappeared
from the line of sight.

Here, the experts professed to hope, was something Project
Saucer could get its teeth into. The whole flying-saucer mystery
might be explained. The first step was to determine whether the
object was an aircraft that had been partially obscured by a cloud
or whose appearance had been distorted by a rainstorm. Two
hundred and twenty-five civilian and military flight schedules were
analyzed, and it was found that one other plane, an Air Force
C-47, had been near the Eastern airliner at the time the mysterious
object was sighted. Conjecture about the C-47 began to appear
irrelevant, however, when the Macon ground crews agreed with
Chiles and Whitted that the thing they had seen was going much
faster than two hundred miles an hour, and so, unless it dawdled
around somewhere, wouldn't have taken anything like an hour to
get from Macon to Montgomery.

Astronomers went to work on the problem. Dr. Hynek considered the possibility that a brilliant, slow-moving meteor might
be the explanation. Various bits of the apparition's description
encouraged this notion — "orange-red flame," "cigar-shaped," "a
tremendous burst of flame." Unfortunately, the flight schedules
of meteors are not available, and Dr. Hynek had no means of
testing his hypothesis. "It will have to be left to the psychologists
to tell us whether the immediate trail of a bright meteor could
produce the subjective impression of a ship with lighted windows,"
he wrote in a report on his findings. The psychologists expressed
the opinion that a meteor could indeed be mistaken for a space
ship. Dr. Fitts, the Ohio State psychologist, observed that both
Chiles and Whitted were human and therefore as likely to be

victims of mass suggestibility as anyone else. Dr. Fitts told me during a talk I had with him that psychologists are used to the fact that even people of high mental caliber often make mistakes about what they see. "Also, I would like to make the point that pilots are trained to instruments," he said. "They grow very dependent on those instruments, and I don't know whether they are necessarily superior observers without them. I do know that during the war, when I was in the Air Force, pilots frequently gave some pretty odd reports of what they'd seen while flying their missions." Chiles and Whitted readily agreed that their report might be thought odd, but they were still certain that they saw what they saw.

At three o'clock in the afternoon of January 7, 1948, something that looked like "an ice-cream cone topped with red" was sighted over the Godman Air Force Base, at Fort Knox, Kentucky, by several military men and civilians. The Godman Base tower requested a flight of four National Guard F-51s that happened to be aloft in the vicinity to investigate the object. The flight leader, Captain Thomas F. Mantell, a veteran with a splendid combat record, reported sighting the object, saying that it was then flying at half his speed. At three-fifteen, he broke away from his formation to go in pursuit, and within minutes radioed the tower, "I'm closing in now to take a good look. It's directly ahead and above . . . and still moving at about half my speed . . . The thing looks metallic and of tremendous size . . . It's going up now, and forward as fast as I am — that's three hundred and sixty miles an hour. I'm going up to twenty thousand feet, and if I'm no closer, I'll abandon chase." Those were the last words ever heard from Mantell. His body was found later that day in the wreckage of his plane. The Air Force officially expressed the belief that he had blacked out from lack of oxygen and had suffocated before his plane hit the ground.

Five minutes after Mantell broke away from his formation, the other planes put down at Godman Field. One of them was refueled and sent up again. It flew a hundred miles south at heights up to thirty-three thousand feet. The pilot saw nothing. The Project Saucer people at first said they believed that Mantell had chased Venus. Later, they dropped this notion, and still later, influenced by Dr. Hynek, returned to it. Dr. Hynek favored the Venus theory after he learned that a peculiar object had been seen not only over Godman Field that evening but, earlier, at three other scattered points, all of them hundreds of miles away — at the Lockbourne Air Force Base, near Columbus, Ohio; at the Clinton County Air Field, in Wilmington, Ohio; and by a pilot approaching Washington, D.C. These three sightings were made at about the time Venus set, and the object was reported to have been near the point on the horizon where the planet disappeared. "In summing up the evidence presented," Dr. Hynek reported, in part, "we are forced to the conclusion that the object observed in the early evening hours of January 7th, at these widely separated localities was the planet Venus. To assume that a terrestrial object located so high as to be visible simultaneously over a wide area could be of such intrinsic brightness and would be placed essentially at the very position of Venus would be incredible. The stellar magnitude of Venus that day made it twenty-nine times brighter than the bright star Arcturus. Venus, when as bright as this, shining through interstices in a host of clouds, could very easily give the [reported] effect . . . of 'a flaming object with a tail.' " The object Mantell pursued had been sighted during the day; the other observers had seen objects in the early evening. Dr. Hynek conceded that one's eye would be less likely to be caught by the planet in daylight than in darkness, but, he wrote in his report, "Once caught, the sighter might wonder why he had never noticed it before; Venus that day was six times brighter than an equivalent area of sky." Dr. Hynek made another point: "The one piece of evidence that leads this investigator to believe that at the time of Captain Mantell's death he was actually trying to reach Venus is that the object appeared essentially stationary (or moving steadily away from him) and he could not seem to gain on it."

A year and a half later, a similar object presented itself over Godman Field. This time, investigators ascertained the co-ordinates of its position and sent them to Walter L. Moore, Professor of Mathematics at the University of Louisville, and he identified it as Venus.

On the night of October 1, 1948, a twenty-seven-minute dogfight took place between another man of unquestioned ability at finding his way around in the air and a puzzling light in the sky. The man was Lieutenant George F. Gorman, during the Second World War a pilot instructor who trained French cadets, and at the time of the dogfight the manager of a construction company in Fargo, North Dakota. He was flying an F-51, completing a routine patrol for the North Dakota National Guard, and had just asked the tower at the Fargo Municipal Airport for clearance to land when he saw what seemed to be another plane's taillight a thousand yards away. He queried the tower, and the men there reported that the only other aircraft over the field was a Piper Cub. Gorman could see the Cub plainly outlined below him. Curious, he flew toward the light. "It was about six to eight inches in diameter, clear white, and completely round, with a sort of fuzz at the edges," Gorman later told investigators, adding that he saw "no outline of anything" around the edges. "It was blinking on and off. As I approached, however, the light suddenly became steady and pulled into a sharp left bank . . . I dived after it and brought my manifold pressure up to sixty inches, but I couldn't catch up with the thing. It started gaining altitude and again made a left bank. I put my F-51 into a sharp turn and tried to cut the light off in its turn. By then, we were at about seven thousand feet. Suddenly it made a sharp right turn and we headed straight at each other. Just when we were about to collide, I guess I got scared. I went into a dive and the light passed over my canopy at about five hundred feet. Then it made a left circle about a thousand feet above, and I gave chase again." Gorman followed the light up to fourteen thousand feet, where, after another near collision, his ship went into a power stall and the light disappeared to the northwest. Gorman noticed no sounds or exhaust-trail odors. He had gunned his plane up to four hundred miles an hour without gaining on the light. It was able to maintain an extremely steep angle of ascent, far greater than that of his Air Force fighter. "When I attempted to turn with [the light], I blacked out temporarily, due to excessive speed," he said. "I am in fairly good physical condition and I do not believe there are many, if any, pilots who could withstand the turn and speed effected by that light and remain conscious."

Project Saucer suspected that Gorman was tilting with a weather balloon. For one thing, it learned that the Fargo weather station had released a lighted balloon only ten minutes before Gorman's patrol stopped being routine. The object's steady, practically vertical climb suggested the behavior of a balloon. A technician who once worked on Project Saucer told me recently that chasing a weather balloon with an airplane is comparable to diving to the bottom of a pool after a hollow rubber ball that has been submerged and then let loose. "You swim around underwater looking for it, but all the time the ball is steadily rising to the surface, and your own zigzagging maneuvers cause you to lose track of the ball and to think that it is eluding you, although it is actually going in a straight course ahead of you," the technician said. "It's very difficult for a pilot to separate target motion and his own motion, even in daylight. At night, it's just about impossible." The balloon theory was buttressed a month and a half later when another nocturnal tangle took place between an Air Force pilot and a lighted object over Andrews Field, near Washington, D.C. The pilot's account of his quarry's evasive tactics was almost identical with Gorman's. This time, it was established that the object was a balloon cluster, set loose by cosmic-ray researchers. Dr. Fitts was so sure that both pilots had been misled by deceptive relative motion that he recommended that the Project Saucer command conduct a controlled experiment with a weather balloon at Wright Field, in which the pilot would not only have the advantage of daylight but would know what he was after. The pilot who made this test duplicated the maneuvers that Gorman had made in pursuing his fuzzy phantom, proving that it was quite possible for an observer in an aircraft to think that the balloon is trying to elude him although it is actually almost stationary or slowly rising in a straight line. Gorman's target, however, despite the circumstantial evidence, was listed as "unidentified."

"Unidentified" is a designation that Project Saucer, which has often had occasion to use it, has always loathed. "As long as anything is called that," Major Boggs said to me, "people can continue to indulge their fantasies." "Unidentified" is a charitable word for some of the will-o'-the-wisps the Project was called upon to explain. In Hamel, Minnesota, two children told of seeing a strange object fall into a back yard where they were playing. It had "spun around once, made a whistling noise, and then shot straight up into the sky about twenty feet, where it stopped again and made more whistling noises." Unidentified. One evening, four residents of Logan, Utah, saw twelve flying objects that looked like birds but were moving awfully fast for birds. Unidentified. Two elderly gentlemen of San Pablo, California, gazing up at a hazy sky, spotted a large, translucent object, which they estimated to be a mile above the earth. An investigator for Project Saucer was sent to interview them. One of the men thought the object resembled an immense amoeba covered with canvas; the other said it looked to him like a vegetable crate. One said it had been going east; the other said it had been going northwest. Both usually wore glasses but hadn't happened to have them on at the time. Unidentified.

In the few instances in which bits and pieces of suspect objects were picked up and turned over to the experts of Project Saucer during the two publicized years of its existence, the fragments were quickly identified. For example, soon after Kenneth Arnold sighted those nine tailless aircraft near Mount Rainier, residents of Jackson, Ohio, excitedly reported the discovery of a fallen disk. Examination showed it was the remains of a Signal Corps weather balloon. Early in 1948, residents of Kansas, southern Nebraska, and northern Oklahoma reported a violent explosion, high in the sky, that shook buildings and broke windows. Project Saucer was, of course, immediately involved. The likeliest clue came from a farmer who lived near Stockton, Kansas. He said that he and his wife had seen a fire in the sky and then a large cloud, after which they heard the big explosion. Two months later, an astronomer, following a hunch, found embedded in the soil forty miles from Stockton the presumed explanation of the mystery — a thousand-pound chunk of an achondrite, an unusual type of meteorite. Smaller pieces were found near by. Some citizens of Bellefontaine, Ohio, thought they had witnessed the disintegration of a flying saucer when a flaming "wheel" fell in their vicinity. Upon analysis at a Wright Field laboratory, what remained of it was found to contain zinc, magnesium, sodium, and lead — standard components of various types of military flares.

For a time in the spring of 1949, it looked as though a Colorado rancher had been harboring a piece of a flying saucer for three years. Back in April 1946 the rancher, riding his horse on a high, rocky mesa, had come across a bit of tattered rigging attached to a steel ring. He took it back to his house, tossed it into a closet, and forgot about it. Then, belatedly reflecting on the wave of saucer sightings, he recalled the contraption in his closet. He showed it to two friends, one of whom, an omniscient type, stated definitely that it was part of a flying saucer. "I've seen too many saucers not to know one when I'm holding one in my own hand," he said. The rancher forwarded his find to Wright Field, where it was identified as a remnant of one of the incendiary balloons the hopeful Japanese dispatched across the Pacific during the war in an effort to start forest fires.

Even pictures taken of supposed saucers failed to impress the experts. There was the case of a man in Phoenix, Arizona, who spotted a flat gray object spiraling up and down in the sky at a speed that he estimated at between four and five hundred miles an hour. He snapped two pictures of it with his Brownie. Prints were rushed to Project Saucer, and Dr. Irving Langmuir, the physicist and a Nobel Prize winner, was asked to study them. The distinguished scientist learned that a thunderstorm had occurred just before the picture-taking, and concluded that he was looking at a couple of rather poor shots of a piece of paper being buffeted by the wind.

As time went on and the skies, apparently, continued to teem with flying saucers, the generals in the Pentagon, warming to their task, decided to enlarge the scope of the investigation. Commanders of all Air Force installations in the country were ordered to assign Intelligence officers to look into sightings reported in their areas. The officers were instructed to solicit the assistance of municipal police officials, who might be familiar with the personalities of the saucer observers. The F.B.I. was also called upon for assistance, and assigned agents to help interview people who reported that they had seen disks. The agents used a standard questionnaire, drawn up by Air Force Intelligence, which called for such information as the saucer's size, speed, color, and maneuvers. The information was usually transmitted to Wright Field, but some stories were so obviously false and some "evidence" so obviously trifling that the F.B.I. men didn't even bother to fill out the questionnaire. In Seattle, for instance, an alarmed woman called the police to inform them that a flaming disk had landed on her roof. The object turned out to be a hollow, drum-shaped affair made of plywood, with "USSR" crudely daubed on it in paint. An F.B.I. man found that a turpentine-soaked cloth had caused the flame. A practical joke, he decided. A farmer near Danforth, Illinois, reported that a saucer had crash-landed in one of his fields and burned up a patch of weeds. The F.B.I. man there concluded that someone had been playing a prank when he found that the disk was an amateur-ish assembly of some old radio parts. When Louella Parsons wrote in her syndicated column that a Hollywood producer had taken some pictures of flying saucers in Alaska, two worldly F.B.I. agents quickly ascertained that a movie company was making a picture about flying saucers in Alaska.

It became common practice among F.B.I. agents, in their efforts to establish the reliability of someone who claimed he had seen a space ship or a flying saucer, to talk with the person's neigh-bors, business associates, friends, and enemies. For instance, after Dale Stevens, a sportswriter on the Richmond, Indiana, *Palladium-Item,* reported simply, and with a restraint uncommon in such matters, that he had seen a hovering light in the eastern sky that looked five or ten times larger than a star, an agent interviewed his publisher and noted, "Employer considers Mr. S. honest and sincere. Mr. S. is a member of the local Junior Chamber of Com-merce." (Stevens' credibility received another endorsement some time later, when Dr. Hynek informed Project Saucer that it was quite possible that Stevens, and not a Sydney, Australia, astrono-mer, was the discoverer of Comet L. 1949 — a recent visitor from space.)

The investigation of one flying-saucer report, which proved to be a hoax, resulted in the death of two Air Force Intelligence officers. Two residents of Tacoma got in touch with the editor of a Chicago adventure magazine and tried to sell him a story about six flying disks they claimed to have seen while they were in a boat off Maury Island; they had been showered with fragments from one of the disks, they said, and a pet dog who was with them had been killed. The editor asked Kenneth Arnold, who, as the first to report seeing a saucer, had by this time become known as the Man Who Saw the Men from Mars, to check on the details of the story. Arnold talked to the men and then asked the Air Force to help him investigate their statements. Two Air Force officers were sent to Tacoma to question the men. The Tacoma men turned over what they said were some of the fragments of the disk. The next day, the investigators took off in a B-25 for Hamilton Field, at San Rafael, California, where they planned to have the fragments analyzed by mineralogists. The plane crashed, and the investigators were killed; the pilot and the only other man aboard parachuted to safety. Soon afterward, newspapers and wire services in Tacoma received anonymous telephone calls telling them that saboteurs had shot down the plane with a 20-mm. cannon, because of the strategic value of its cargo. Actually, flames from a burned-out exhaust had set fire to the left wing of the plane. A few days later, the Tacoma pair, under further questioning, confessed that they had taken the fragments from an unusual rock formation they found on Maury Island. They had simply made up the flying-disk story.

On one occasion, an F.B.I. agent stationed in Denver himself described a strange object in the sky. After a hard day at the office, he was driving home when he spotted an unaccountable light over the city's airport. He got out of his car and collected a group of witnesses, all of whom agreed that the light was about five miles above the earth and traveling eastward. He made a report to the Air Force, and it assigned him to investigate his own story. He started by visiting the airport the next evening. He was standing around describing his experience to some local fliers when he suddenly pointed up to the sky and shouted, "There it is!" What he saw was the night light on a weather balloon. The Weather Bureau station at the airport sent one up at the same time every evening.

The scientists attached to Project Saucer examined the results of all investigations that seemed to contain clues that belonged in their respective fields. The reports they made on them were filed in the Pentagon, and Major Boggs let me read a number of them. The first one I read was by Dr. Fitts, who pointed out that one of the first tenets of psychology is that human perception is fallible. He outlined the mechanics of optical illusion and told of the irrationalizing effects of vertigo, a kind of blacking-out to which any of us is subject. Asserting that every saucer report that had not been proved to be a hoax or a case of mistaken identity could be explained on psychological grounds, he challenged practically all the data that had been submitted by observers. How, he asked, could anyone tell how far away a saucer was if he didn't know its size? How could anyone presume to estimate an object's speed without knowing its distance from himself? He suggested that some of the sightings might be blamed on *muscae volitantes* (flitting flies), the medical term for small solid particles that float about in the fluid of the eye, casting a shadow on the retina and moving as the eye moves.

Other elements of the saucer problem were studied by such men as Dr. George Valley, a nuclear physicist at the Massachusetts Institute of Technology; staff members of the research firm of Rand Corporation; an assortment of physicists and aerodynamicists who specialize in the study of the stratosphere and the space beyond it; and the electronics experts attached to the Cambridge Field Station. These men were all searching for physical rather than psychological explanations, and some fairly strange theories occurred to them — the possibility that extraterrestrial animals were flying into our atmosphere, for example. (No data turned up to support that arresting idea.) The theory that the saucers were hostile aircraft was carefully studied and rejected. "The performances of these saucers not only surpass the development of present science but the development of present fiction-science writers," one scientist noted. The specialists also considered and rejected the concept of disks capable of riding the air on beams or rays of some kind. They even speculated on whether the anti-gravity shield that H. G. Wells thought up for his novel *The First Men in the Moon* would work; it wouldn't, they decided. The supposition that interplanetary craft were whizzing in at us was also discredited, despite its popularity with laymen. Space ships, the scientists thought, would have to be so large and unwieldy that they couldn't possibly zigzag as frivolously as the reported saucers did. Besides, a space ship, regardless of its size, could not, in the opinion of these men, carry sufficient fuel to remain for any length of time in the earth's dense atmosphere. The scientists noted, too, that the supposed spacemen showed a remarkable lack of interest in the rest of the world, being, it would seem, almost unanimous in their desire to see America first. "The small area covered by the disk barrage points strongly to the belief that the flying objects are of earthly origin, be they physical or psychological," one of the scientists reported.

From the report turned in by the astronomers, I learned that they, in addition to seining out comets, meteors, bolides, and achondrites from the stream of objects people were seeing in the skies, had also thoughtfully considered our planetary neighbors. The old question of the possibility of life on Mars took on a new urgency, and a new corollary: If there *are* living creatures on Mars, would they be capable of building space ships? The astronomers thought not. Their perhaps slightly anthropomorphic conclusion was that Mars is so desolate and inhospitable that any living beings there would be intent on merely existing; they wouldn't have time to think of space ships, even in order to transport themselves to a better climate.

Venus, regarded as the innocent cause of several reports of flying saucers, was also considered as a launching site for them. The astronomers concluded that its atmosphere, believed to be composed largely of carbon dioxide and immense, opaque clouds of formaldehyde droplets, precluded the practice of astronomy, and hence the concept of a universe and the idea of space ships. The speculations of the astronomers were not confined to the solar system. They took into consideration not only the planets in the solar system but the twenty-two stars in addition to the sun that are thought to have satellites revolving around them. In view of the distance between these stars and the earth, the astronomers admitted frankly that their earth-bound minds bogged down at the thought of anything traveling that far. "The nearest eligible star is one called Wolf 359," an astronomer prominent in this phase of the investigation noted. "It is eight light-years away. A spaceship pilot taking off from one of that sun's planets and traveling at one-tenth the speed of light — say, at eighteen thousand miles per second — would need eighty years to make a one-way trip to the earth. And that speed is completely beyond the reach of any predicted level of rocket propulsion."

When I had a talk with Major Boggs after reading the reports, he remarked, "You know, not one of these wonder saucers has ever malfunctioned. My God, we have our hands full with conventional planes, but these saucers never seem to get in trouble and have to make forced landings."

After two years of operation, Project Saucer had not accomplished one of its principal objectives — that of satisfying the public that our air was free of unexplainable things. Nevertheless, on December 27, 1949, the Air Force issued a public announcement that Project Saucer was about to be disbanded. Perhaps the

Air Force felt that silence was the best antidote for the contagion of mass susceptibility; whatever its reasons, the fact is that Project Saucer, while it did cease to exist as an agency working hand in hand with the general public, merely underwent an organizational change and then kept right on tracking down, in a considerably more quiet manner, reports of "aerial phenomena," to use its official term. Just one man, stationed at Wright Field and bearing the title of Aerial Phenomena Officer, was assigned to it on a full-time basis, and his orders were to limit his investigations to observations reported by pilots, scientists, engineers, and others who could presumably be considered qualified observers. Whatever information of value he picked up he was to turn over to the authorities at Wright Field. "We changed the study of unidentified flying objects from a special project to a general operation," an Air Force colonel recently told me. "Analyses of the sightings went through normal staff channels, so that our experts found them in their 'in' baskets along with their regular work. Of course, if the Aerial Phenomena Officer needed a kind of expert we didn't have on the payroll at Dayton, we'd put him in touch with the right fellow. In the fall of 1951, I remember, the officer suspected that a formation of lights seen over a southern state might be ducks, so we arranged for him to consult an ornithologist who was an authority on the migratory habits of waterfowl. Well, all we know is they weren't ducks."

The immediate effect of the Air Force's announcement that Project Saucer was about to fold was a decrease in the number of crackpot sightings, but seemingly reliable reports of objects seen in the sky continued to come in. "Not a month has gone by without our receiving reports that seem worth investigating," Captain Edward J. Ruppelt, the Aerial Phenomena Officer, informed me. "I've flown all over the country interviewing people who are as intelligent as any I've ever met. They've been entirely co-operative in talking with me. Some of them say they regret having seen what they saw, because up till then they'd always thought that all this talk of flying saucers was just so much foolishness. They don't want their names publicized, for fear of being ridiculed by their friends and professional colleagues. I always promise them there's no danger of that — that while the information they give me may be made public, their names never will be." In most cases, Captain Ruppelt said, investigation has shown that the people he has interviewed had been deceived by things that have been deceiving others all along — balloons, planes, meteors, and so on — but a nettling residue of around twenty per cent of the cases have wound up in that exasperating old pigeonhole labeled "Unidentified." Nothing, for example, could be found to account for the "something silvery directly overhead" reported by a mystified Civil Aeronautics Administration inspector at Terre Haute. A commercial pilot who, flying near Battle Creek, Michigan, spotted "an oval-shaped silver object" ahead of his ship, posed a similarly unsolved problem, as did a highly respected naval officer, stationed at the dirigible base at Lakehurst, New Jersey, who reported that he had stared through his binoculars at a brilliant image making turns that were far too tight for any known aircraft.

Twenty-five per cent of the observers interrogated by the Aerial Phenomena Officer since early in 1950, have been military pilots. Eight per cent have been commercial pilots, some with as much as twenty years' experience in the air, and at one stage in the current phase of the investigation, even a few physicists at Los Alamos, New Mexico, men who make a fetish of objectivity, were interviewed after they reported having seen puzzling lights hovering above their atomic-energy laboratories. "If you took any one of these incidents by itself, it might not mean much," Captain Ruppelt said. "But in view of the number and caliber of the informants, you couldn't help taking their claims seriously."

In February 1951, Dr. Urner Liddel, a nuclear physicist attached to the Office of Naval Research, at Washington, D.C., declared that at last, thanks to the lifting of certain security restrictions, he could provide the solution to the mystery of the flying saucers: They were "skyhooks," he said — balloons a hundred feet in diameter, which the Navy had secretly been sending up for the past four years in order to study cosmic rays. Dr. Liddel's assertion was immediately disputed by Dr. Anthony O. Mirarchi, who, as former head of the Air Force's Atmospheric Composition Bureau, had assisted in the diagnosis of Project Saucer reports. Dr. Mirarchi said he thought the saucers might be missiles from some foreign country carrying out reconnaissance missions over our atomic-energy plants. Dr. Liddel's explanation also made little impression on two Wright Field pilots, Captains E. W. Spradley and J. E. Cocker, who had seen a baffling something in the sky at a time when they were extremely balloon-conscious. They reported that they were tracking a large weather balloon over Alamogordo, New Mexico, not far from where the first atomic bomb was detonated, when they saw a flat "milky" object near the balloon. They estimated its altitude at between fifty and sixty thousand feet. Suddenly, they said, it gave off "three brilliant flashes, like photo flashes," and disappeared. Nor did Dr. Liddel's statement put a stop to the steady flow of reports of sightings — a "propelled bluish-white star" seen by an American Airlines pilot near Phoenix; "three circles of light spinning counterclockwise" that a Pennsylvania control-tower operator saw above his airport; "globe-shaped orange objects" that airmen over Korea said they saw. "In recent months, our informants have stressed light and color to us," Captain Ruppelt told me. "They rarely talk about disks any more, or anything else that might indicate solidity. That's pretty near the only generalization we've been able to draw from our data. We've tried every possible way to establish patterns for these — well, things. We've plotted them out on maps in an effort to find out if they're concentrated in any particular part of the country. They do seem to be more or less grouped around certain atomic installations, but that point isn't really worth much if you take into account the fact that people in such vital areas are liable to be more watchful of the sky than, say, a taxi driver in New York. We've plotted frequency of sightings by the hour of the day, the day of the week, and the month of the year. We've tried to determine if there isn't at least some common denominator to their shapes and colors. We've done our best to find out if they've been moving in any general direction. We've got nowhere."

In March 1952, Captain Ruppelt's records show, seventeen sightings were reported. In April, the figure rose sharply to ninety, a development that some Air Force people attribute to the publication in *Life* that month of an article entitled "Have We Visitors from Space?" In May, the reports of sightings dropped to seventy, but in June, when *Life* ran a sequel to its April article, they went up to a hundred and eleven. By July, the daily press, which had been fairly restrained about the matter for the past two years, stepped up its number of saucer stories, for the most part of the one-paragraph variety. On July 21st, however, saucers again became front-page news. That was the day a Senior Air Traffic Controller for the Civil Aeronautics Administration at the National Airport's Air Route Traffic Control Center, in Washington, informed the Air Force, and the public, that early that morning his radarscope had picked up ten unidentifiable objects flying over various parts of the capital, including the prohibited area around the White House.

Shortly after midnight, the controller, Harry G. Barnes, related in a newspaper article that appeared under his signature, one of his crew of eight had asked him to look at the radarscope, jocularly remarking, "Here's a fleet of flying saucers for you." Barnes looked and saw seven "pips" — pale-violet spots that are supposed to represent aircraft but in this case were behaving like no plane pips Barnes had ever observed. They followed no set course, kept no formation, and could be tracked for only about three miles at a time, instead of the orthodox twenty-five or thirty, before disappearing from the screen. They seemed to be moving at a speed of between a hundred and a hundred and thirty miles an hour. At times, they moved together in a cluster, at other times wandered about singly. Barnes had two radar controllers look at the screen and they saw what he did. He had technicians check his radar equipment and they found it in perfect order. He called the airport control tower and the radar operator there said that the same curious pips were showing up on his screen.

One of Barnes' men then radioed Captain S. C. Pierman, who had been a Capital Airlines pilot for seventeen years and who had just taken off from the Washington airport, asking him to look for the objects. In a short while, Pierman radioed back, "There's one, and there it goes." During the next fourteen minutes, Pierman saw six bright lights that resembled tailless shooting stars, but three of them were moving horizontally, unlike any shooting star he had ever seen. Another commercial pilot who was reached in flight near by said that he saw a light off his left wing; Barnes found a corresponding pip on the radarscope. Other pilots in the vicinity reported, however, that they could see nothing unusual. Toward daybreak, ten peculiar pips were counted simultaneously on Barnes' screen. "There is no other conclusion I can reach but that for six hours on the morning of the twentieth of July there were at least ten unidentifiable objects moving above Washington," Barnes wrote. "They were not ordinary aircraft . . . Nor in my opinion could any natural phenomena account for these spots on our radar. Neither shooting stars, electrical disturbances, nor clouds could, either. Exactly what they are, I don't know. Now you know as much about them as I do. And your guess is as good as mine."

A week later, at 9:08 p.m. on July 26th, the Air Route Traffic Control Center's radarscope again showed unidentifiable objects over Washington. So did the screen at the Andrews Air Force Base, just outside the capital. Two jet interceptors, capable of doing six hundred miles an hour, were dispatched from a base near New Castle, Delaware, to investigate. When the interceptors appeared on the radarscopes, they were guided toward the objects. One of the pilots sighted four lights approximately ten miles in front of his plane and slightly above it, but they vanished while he was trying to overtake them. Twenty minutes later, he saw "a steady white light," but within a minute it, too, disappeared. "We have no evidence they were flying saucers," an Air Force representative said later. "Conversely, we have no evidence they were not flying saucers. We don't know what they were."

As a result of these two incidents, particularly the one involving the interceptors, public agitation reached a new height. The Air Force was bombarded with hundreds of letters, telephone calls, and telegrams demanding information and offering advice. One of the smaller airlines supplied its crews with cameras and ordered them to photograph any saucers they encountered. A civilian wrote to the Air Force that he would let it in on "the secret" in return for a colonelcy. A Los Angeles pastor wrote to Einstein, beseeching him to clear up the mystery, and Einstein wrote back, "Dear Sir: Those people have seen something. What it is I do not know and I am not curious to know." The Civil Defense director of Nassau County, Long Island tried to recruit members for his Ground Observer Corps by announcing, "Here is a chance for everyone to get first-hand knowledge of the flying-saucer hokum. All observers will be able to discern the difference between or among the sun, moon, stars, meteorites, searchlight beams, weather balloons, propeller and jet aircraft." Two Wisconsin disc jockeys, who apparently had never heard of Orson Welles, told their audience that they had found a saucer with a two-foot man inside; the management of the station spent the next day or so broadcasting assurances that it had all been just a gag.

Many communications received by the Air Force have dealt

with the question of whether or not the saucers should be shot down. Some letter writers urged the Air Force to knock the lights out of the sky — assuming, of course, that the lights weren't United States property. The majority, however, were for making friends with the visitors. "Why should we be the first to kill?" one correspondent inquired plaintively. A twelve-year-old girl implored the Air Force to spare "the Saucerians," and a Unitarian minister in Massachusetts asked, "Why not entice them to land? The attitude of our people (and the Air Force) seems to me to be outwardly very immature with reference to these visitors to our planet. It seems to me that a very little publicity with a friendly slant to it would entirely change the picture . . . Isn't it worth a try?" The possibility that the visitors might not consider it an unmitigated blessing to be invited to land here was suggested by a distinguished theologian. In an article written for the National Catholic Welfare Conference News Service, the Very Reverend Francis J. Connell, Dean of the School of Sacred Theology at Catholic University, in Washington, D.C., declared that if rational beings do exist on other worlds, and if they have supernatural and preternatural gifts and have never sinned, they may be living in a state of paradise. "With their preternatural gifts, it would be reasonable to suppose they would be far ahead of us technically," Father Connell wrote. "With their superior intellect they might well have mastered interplanetary travel. If these supposed rational beings should possess the immortality of body once enjoyed by Adam and Eve, it would be foolish for our super-jet or rocket pilots to attempt to shoot them. They would be unkillable."

In an effort to quiet the gathering tumult, Major John A. Samford, the present head of Air Force Intelligence, submitted to a press conference a few days after the jet chase over Washington. Major General Roger M. Ramey, the Air Force's Operations Director, was present, as were several Intelligence officers, including

Captain Ruppelt. General Samford was by turn grave, skeptical, defensive, and informative. He didn't consider the radar incidents unusual. He said that over the past few years Air Force interceptors had made hundreds of fruitless responses to radar pips. Birds, balloons, ionized clouds, and light civilian planes had been their usual harvest. Radar had been designed for dealing primarily with aircraft, he said, but as more and more is learned about the device, perhaps it may offer possibilities for scientific observation of a nature for which it was never intended.

General Samford suggested that "temperature inversion" might have been responsible for the radar pips, especially since for quite a while there had been hot, humid air over Washington. As a result of temperature inversion, the General explained, with the help of an aide who was an electronics expert, radar sometimes makes objects that are actually on the ground look as if they were in the air; inversion takes place when a warm layer of air comes in over a cool one, increasing the density of the cool one so that it will bend light rays. In the region where the two layers meet, an atmospheric reflector, or "overhead mirror," is formed, creating some curious mirages. The General recalled the experience of the pilot of a night fighter who, while using his radar to follow an object apparently in flight, suddenly found himself heading straight for the ground. The pilot had pulled out barely in time.

The "highest probability" concerning the saucers, General Samford stated, is that they are phenomena associated with "intellectual and scientific interests that we are on the road to learn more about." The real difficulty in disposing of the reports about them has been that none of the reports to date have contained measurements made by standard devices that could "convert the thing or the idea of the phenomenon into something that becomes manageable as material for any kind of analysis that we know." Incidentally, the General pointed out, astronomers, whom he called "our best advisers . . . in this business of visitors from elsewhere," photograph the sky continuously, but they had reported no saucers. The General was reminded that many of the people who had told of seeing the most spectacular things were considered the most reliable. He replied that he had no intention of discrediting them, but the fact remained that none of them had offered data of the kind a scientist would find useful. An Air Force officer whom General Samford personally knew to be a competent witness had told him of seeing a saucer in the Middle East. This man, too, had been unable to obtain accurate measurements. "We have many reports from credible observers of incredible things," the General remarked.

Like General Moore, his predecessor in Project Saucer days, General Samford denied that the Air Force was attempting to cover up secret experiments. When he was asked if the saucers might be the guided missiles of a foreign country, he replied that he didn't see how, on the basis of their weird performances, they could be unless "someone" had achieved a means of developing unlimited power — "power of such fantastic higher limits that it is a theoretical unlimited; it's not anything that we can understand" — and utilizing it under conditions in which no mass is involved. As for the latter, the General told the press, drawing a laugh, "You know, what 'no mass' means is that there's nothing there."

While General Samford's interview probably reassured the public as evidence that the Air Force was still on the job, it did nothing to lessen the nation's saucer-consciousness. The reporters had hardly thanked the General for his comments when, on August 1, 1952, a Coast Guard photographer produced a picture showing four bizarre lights burning brilliantly in a daylight sky. He said he had taken it over Salem, Massachusetts. The next day, a Harvard astrophysicist called the photograph worthless because it was accompanied by no scientific data, such as temperature distribution and altitude. On August 6th, an Army physicist at Fort Belvoir, Virginia, created the equivalent of flying saucers in his laboratory by introducing molecules of ionized air into a partial vacuum in a bell jar, and three days later an internationally known authority on atmospheric conditions said of the physicist's experiment, "I know of no conditions of the earth's atmosphere, high or low, which would duplicate those needed to make the laboratory models." That same summer, a number of newspapers printed rumors that an Air Force plane had shot down a flying saucer, and the United Press, quoting a Cleveland paper, said that the plane had been "repeatedly attacked" by the saucer. An Omaha man wrote the Air Force that the saucers were God's way of tormenting us for having deified science; a man in Kansas City, Kansas, saw their visitation as an occasion for rejoicing. He cited Ezekiel 10:4: "Then the glory of the Lord went up from the cherub, and stood over the threshold of the house; and the house was filled with the cloud, and the court was full of the brightness of the Lord's glory."

In mid-1954, more competent observers than ever before were reporting saucers, Captain Ruppelt's successor, a Captain Charles Hardin, told me. The Air Force was buying a hundred special cameras, which it hoped would help determine what the provocative objects were made of, and it was considering buying several photographic telescopes of a new type, costing as much as five thousand dollars apiece, with which a continuous photographic record could be made nightly of the sky over the whole hemisphere. After the better part of a decade and close to three thousand reported sightings of a serious nature, there was no discussion in Air Force circles of abandoning the pursuit of the elusive saucers. Too many people were waiting for the answer.

iii

BOMBS AWAY!

WHETHER OR NOT flying saucers exist, there is no debating the reality of an exploding atomic bomb, certainly not the one I, along with three hundred or so other reporters, public officials, and civil-defense people, saw go off at Yucca Flat, Nevada. Undoubtedly one of the most exciting moments of the test — in which an atomic bomb was used for the first time as part of a tactical troop maneuver — occurred forty-two seconds before the detonation, when Dr. Gaelen Felt, a thin young scientist who had been briefing us spectators assembled at the foot of an ugly, boulder-encrusted knoll overlooking a section of the Nevada desert, calmly announced over the public-address system, "Bombs away!" By that time, having heeded Dr. Felt's warning of eighteen seconds before, we were all staring blindly into special goggles approximately ten times as opaque as ordinary sunglasses. In the blackness, various images absorbed during the past hour of waiting were still fresh enough to be remembered clearly: the smooth, sandy miles of Yucca Flat, the dried-out salt lake where the target area was; a helicopter, which was going to take up a radiological-survey team twenty minutes after the burst, landing at the edge of the desert basin, not far from the observers' hill; the almost cloudless morning sky, streaked with the vapor trails, thirty-two thousand feet up, left by the B-50 that was carrying the bomb, as it made practice runs over the target; the bustle accompanying the deployment of the spectators and participants — the observers ten miles from the target; fifteen hundred troops, whom the bomb would theoretically help capture a hostile strong point, in trenches and foxholes four miles from the target; and, well ahead of the troops, serving as advance elements against the invisible enemy, sixteen hundred mice and twenty-four anesthetized pigs, who would wake up late that afternoon in a near-by laboratory, to find curious biologists examining them.

After Dr. Felt's "Bombs away!," however, a new and apocryphal image abruptly intruded itself in my mind — a free-falling atomic bomb (an unclassified model, I suspect). When Dr. Felt shouted "Zero!," a light that turned the world to sun engulfed my goggles. Simultaneously, I was startled by a jet of heat licking at me. (A scientist told me later that the temperature of the air had momentarily risen from eighty-three degrees to a hundred and forty, which was not surprising, because the temperature of the bomb's blast was nearly two million degrees.) Dr. Felt had advised us to count off three seconds before removing our goggles, and I heard myself doing so aloud. As I pulled mine off, Dr. Felt told us not to move, that a shock wave was approaching. A few seconds later, a sharp, jarring thunderclap struck down at our hill from the sunny sky, and Dr. Felt was through with his warnings for the day. My first relatively unworried look at the target area filled me with a guilty aestheticism. Beautiful peach, violet, and pink streamers, produced by the combining of nitrogen and oxygen, had been left behind by the so-called ball of fire, a spherical caldron, nine hundred feet in diameter, that was churning upward. Below the ball of fire, in hopeless pursuit, was a column of dust, five thousand feet high, that had been sucked out of Yucca Flat. Five minutes after the burst, Dr. Felt announced that the atomic cloud had attained a height of thirty-five thousand feet. Not far from where I was standing, a radio broadcaster, barking like a coxswain into his microphone, fastened onto the word "mushroom" and couldn't seem to let go. The man next to me, Merrill Eisenbud, a radiation-monitoring expert who was not involved with the test, disagreed sharply with the broadcaster. "That's no mushroom — that's a Portuguese man-of-war," he said. "Look at those ice tentacles coming down from the cloud." The broadcaster finally shifted to "an enormous, enormous cloud," "a cataract of white waves," and "a glowing mass of energy," but Eisenbud still wasn't satisfied. "Sounds terrific," he said to me. "Wish I'd seen it."

The smell of burning sagebrush had long since reached our hill, and now, in the distance on Yucca Flat, I could make out several distinct fires. Airplanes and Army vehicles, left there to test the weapon's effect on them, were smoldering. A small first-aid shack three miles from the target — far enough to have been considered "safe" — was sending up black smoke. The helicopter with the radiological-survey team took off, and a short while later a second helicopter came spinning toward us and landed directly in front of our hill. From it emerged a lieutenant general, who strode past us halfway up the knoll, turned around, and delivered a talk. He had been up forward with the troops, he said, and the boys had made jokes immediately before and after the explosion. The weapon, he declared, had to be regarded as so much firepower. From a tactical point of view, he went on clinically, the day's bomb had been too big, because it had prevented the troops from advancing quickly enough. "We learned in the war that you have to follow close behind your firepower to capture your objective," he said.

After he finished speaking, I looked for the atomic cloud, but it had floated off and was now indistinguishable from other white flecks in the sky. Eisenbud couldn't pick it out, either. Whichever fleck it was, he informed me, it would drift south, then northeast. "It should be over northern Mexico by tonight," he said authoritatively. "Five days from now, thoroughly dissipated, it'll be over New York, and we'll have nothing more to worry about."

Spectacular and frightening as the burst had been, I left the proving ground with a troubling sense of detachment about the whole demonstration. Comparing notes with some of the other observers, I found that I was not alone. We agreed that we could blame this disturbing reaction, at least in part, on our safe vantage point, but the feeling persisted that the weapon had not seemed quite as terrible as we had anticipated. Back in Las Vegas, later that day, I mentioned this to the director of the test, Dr. Alvin C. Graves, a blue-eyed physicist of forty-two, whose vision is gradually deteriorating as the result of a radiation accident six years ago at the Los Alamos Scientific Laboratory, in New Mexico. Dr. Graves, who is an active churchman in Los Alamos, told me that he had had this feeling in the past himself, and had often worried about it; he added, with a smile, that it was elusive enough for him to go right on stewing over. A certain degree of detachment was appropriate, he believed. He didn't think people ought to be panicked by the mere existence of the bomb, the way they were in 1946. It was a fact of life, he said, and had to be lived with, like a heart condition. On the other hand, the weapon was too formidable to allow for very much detachment. Of course, he said, getting back to the morning's detonation, we had watched a test, not an attack on a city. The bomb had generated more energy than those used at Hiroshima, Nagasaki, and Bikini. We would never know how many people might have been killed by its neutrons or gamma rays; no buildings had been toppled by winds traveling at several hundred miles an hour. The desert was fire-proofed with sand, but a city would have been a holocaust. Dr. Graves said that he and his colleagues had no way of measuring such hypothetical calamities, although on a few occasions, both in Nevada and at Eniwetok, they had tried to do so, in a limited way, by erecting more or less standard structures on which to test the weapon's effects. There had been times when, despite the expense it would have entailed, they had seriously considered building a model of a large city and then bombing it. The idea had been discarded because of the impossibility of arriving at any precise answers. "There aren't any two cities alike," he explained. "There aren't even two buildings alike. Each of them is different from the rest, just as each man's body is."

The detonation of the bomb — the sixteenth exploded on this continent — was, naturally, the reason for the descent on Las Vegas of governors, mayors, civil-defense officials, and newspapermen, but the event was preceded by three days of activities that in some cases were hardly conducive to thinking of the bomb as either an intellectual achievement or a stupendous menace. The night before the test, at a lavish cocktail party given by the Flamingo Hotel, the out-of-town observers were inducted into the Ancient and Honorable Society of Atomic-Bomb Watchers, Las Vegas Local No. 1. A builder by the name of Hal B. Hayes flew in from Los Angeles and called a press conference to announce that he had developed a bombproof house featuring egg-shaped shutters to protect the windows. The Governor of Nevada, welcoming the visitors, said that among his constituents the previous explosions on Yucca Flat hadn't caused "any more commotion than someone winning a jackpot in Las Vegas."

On the whole, though, thanks to the planning of the Atomic Energy Commission, the three days were spent quite purposefully. The better part of one day was taken up with a series of lectures delivered in the Las Vegas City Hall auditorium by scientists associated with the test. The men were extremely informative, as would be expected, but their uncertainties were occasionally more impressive than their facts. Dr. Norris Bradbury, the Director of the Los Alamos Scientific Laboratory, in making the point that it was difficult to foretell how a particular nuclear device would behave, disclosed that the Alamogordo explosion in 1945 had proved to be twice as powerful as anticipated. Another expert said that the larger weapons were being tested at Eniwetok rather than in the United States "because we don't want to take any chances." When the president of the Sandia Corporation, the ordnance-engineering firm operated by Western Electric for the Atomic Energy Commission, was asked from the floor to compare the physical damage produced by small and large explosions, he replied, "We may get more damage from small releases than large ones. Shock waves are rather unpredictable things." Dr. Everett F. Cox, an authority on blast effects, concluded his address by saying, "The A.E.C. agencies have been fortunate in that no damage has been done so far by shocks that have traveled through the ozonosphere. Damage can be done by ozonosphere shocks, as the Pacific Fleet learned in 1931, when gun practice off Catalina Island broke windows in Bakersfield. We are continuing our investigations to learn more about ozonosphere shocks and so be better able to predict where they will strike." Lieutenant Colonel J. B. Hartgering, a doctor of medicine specializing in radiological safety, after assuring the observers that the radioactive atomic cloud was unlikely to pass over the spot where they would be stationed and shower them with particles, added, "However, wind and weather conditions are always unpredictable. In case of a sudden shift in the target-area winds, or the occurrence of something unforeseen, all arrangements have been made for an orderly evacuation. Explicit instructions will be given over the public-address system."

In addition to attending the lectures, we visited a near-by airfield used by elements of the 4925th Test Group (Atomic), the unit whose planes drop the bombs and also sample the atomic clouds and then track them for six hundred miles, in order to warn off pilots of other aircraft, who might mistake drifting radioactivity for an ordinary cloud. While I was at the airbase, a very young-looking pilot sounded me out on an idea he and his fellows had been kicking around. "We're considering painting a little white cloud on our planes for each of our test missions," he said. "What do you think?"

We also toured the proving ground, where the prize attraction turned out to be an air-conditioned underground bunker filled with oscilloscopes and other electronic equipment for recording data during a burst. The bunker, which was well within the destructive range of the target area, has a concrete ceiling that is six feet thick and covered with twelve feet of earth topped by macadam. Its walls, also concrete, are four feet thick. Its entrance, which is labyrinthine, is protected by a two-inch hollow steel door, filled with lead, that weighs three tons. I asked Roy A. Norman, a technician who was showing us around, if he thought a man could survive in the bunker during a test. "He might, but I wouldn't want to be the fellow," he said. "I'd go nuts waiting for the instruments to start clicking with timing signals just before the shot. I wouldn't want to be leaning against a wall after the shot, not unless I wanted my head bashed against it by a shock wave. And I'd be awfully wary about coming out, no matter who telephoned me it was all right."

Of the various officials I talked with during the tours and between lectures, none awaited the impending test more eagerly than the civil-defense people. "We're counting heavily on this bomb," one of them told me. "It's a tough job selling accident insurance." Another thought that the explosion would greatly boost the morale of his organization but regretted that only seventy-five invitations had been allotted to its members. "Some of those ladies with station wagons are sore as hell at us," he said. "You can't blame them. This shot is going to be something to talk about for a long, long time."

Eight hours after the detonation, a hundred troops who had been in the foxholes and trenches that morning were marched into the City Hall auditorium. They were ranged against the walls in groups, by states, for the convenience of newspapermen interested in local stories. Almost instantly, the barnlike structure was alive with the din of feature stories. I wandered down one of the aisles, listening to snatches of the interviews, and found that the atomic G.I. sounded very much like his counterpart of a few years ago. An Arizona boy had prayed. A chipper California man said that he'd take the atomic bomb any day over those German 88s he'd known in Sicily. An Illinois corporal said that he'd drawn a stranger as his foxhole mate, but that after the hot earthquake they'd experienced together he was sure they'd be buddies for life. A very young blond New York City corporal wanted the reporter talking to him to do him a favor. "My name is Geiger, Vincent Geiger," he said, "and all the fellows in my company keep asking me if my father's the guy who invented that counter. I would appreciate it if you wrote that he isn't." The most hopeful, though unconsciously hopeful, words I heard were uttered by a New Mexican, an earnest, swarthy private first class named Evaristo Hernandez. "I passed up my furlough to be in on this test," he told his interviewer. "I figured I might never have another chance to see an atom bomb."

A day or so later, I ran into Dr. Graves at the local offices of the Atomic Energy Commission. He had only a minute to spare, and he spent it talking some more about detachment. Perhaps what had dismayed me and the others on leaving the proving ground, he said, hadn't been indifference about the bomb but an awareness that our imaginations had limits. That, he assured me, smiling, had been a trait of human beings for a long time. It certainly applied to him, and he knew the exact pressure measurements of each bomb that was being exploded. "I can give precise answers to precise questions about the weapon," he said, "but what all of us want are precise answers to vague questions. We want to know what to do about the bomb — what will happen to our homes? How can I answer this? Just ask me precise questions."

iv

BLACKJACK AND FLASHES

THE PROVING GROUND at Yucca Flat, where I witnessed the detonation, is probably the only atomic-energy installation in the country that tallies to any great extent with the layman's conception of such projects. The other manifestations of the thriving new industry — factories producing radioactive fuels, piles cooking fissionable materials, laboratories housing novel research equipment, and so on — have thus far turned out to be eerily silent and generally as well-behaved as a hosiery mill. At Yucca Flat, sixty-five miles northwest of Las Vegas, in the desert of southern Nevada, there is a bit of action. Neither the tight security watch that is maintained over the government-owned proving ground nor the distance between it and Las Vegas, where I spent considerable time both before and after attending the shot at Yucca Flat, has prevented taxpayers in the vicinity from getting at least a sketchy idea of the nature of the product they are helping to finance. On numerous occasions since the proving ground was started in the winter of 1951, a piercing flash of light, many times the intensity of the sun's, has burst over the proving ground in the very early morning, momentarily transforming a gloomy Nevada dawn to a

65

dazzling noon. The same light, pale and diminished, has been seen simultaneously as far away as San Diego, on the Pacific Coast, and Kalispell, Montana — three hundred and fifty and a thousand miles, respectively, from the proving ground. The atomic clouds, with their unearthly hues, that accompany nuclear detonations have been plainly visible from Las Vegas, and sound, in the form of shock waves, has hurtled into this mecca of gamblers, divorcees, and elopers, cracking hotel walls and demolishing restaurant china. Merchants have seen the panes of their display windows shattered and strewn on the sidewalk. After one detonation, the owners of Allen & Hanson, a haberdashery, placed a barrel filled with plateglass fragments outside their shop and posted a sign over it: "ATOM BOMB SOUVENIRS — FREE!" Within an hour, the barrel was empty. At last reports, five hundred sixty-two people in this region have collected damages from the government, amounting to nearly fifty thousand dollars, and additional claims are pending. The detonation of one bomb broke a vase in Modesto, California, five hundred miles from the testing area.

Thanks to their new neighbor, Las Vegans have picked up a little physics. When they see an atomic flash in the sky, they immediately consult their watches, for they have learned that it takes the ensuing shock wave about seven minutes to reach their town from the proving ground. They know, too, that the low-pressure wave that follows a shock wave does not push windows in but sucks them out, and that the best thing to do to escape damage from both waves is to open a window or door. Despite all the rainless lightning and thunder the Las Vegans have been subjected to, it is possible to find among their other reactions a certain pride in their proximity to the proving ground. "It annoys me to read about some statesman saying that the *world* is living with the atomic bomb," a local divorce lawyer told me. "Damn it, it's not the world. It's Las Vegas."

did disturb Las Vegas gamblers. That was in November, 1951, when a plate-glass window near a crap game in the El Cortez Hotel was broken by a shock wave. The players turned briefly to see what had happened and, when they got back to their game, found that the pot was shy twenty dollars.

As word of what was in store for Las Vegas spread, motoring tourists began making it a point to stop there long enough to shop for merchandise, which, they calmly explained, they wanted not for utility but as mementos of a town that archeologists would in all probability soon be exploring. "It got to be pretty grim," a salesman at the local Sears, Roebuck store said to me. "One morning during those last days of waiting, an elderly lady from Los Angeles came in and told me to hurry up and sell her two shirts, that her husband was waiting outside in the car with the motor running. She said she wanted to hand them down to her grandsons, as heirlooms that had come from Las Vegas just before it was wiped off the face of the earth."

To add to the general apprehension, it began to appear that the Commission had decided not to make known in advance the hour, or even the day, when its bombs were to be exploded (a policy it later discarded). Provoked by this, some Las Vegans, upon learning that the local office of the Civil Aeronautics Authority would be responsible for clearing air lanes near the proving ground several hours prior to a detonation, took to calling that office daily, pretending to be pilots of private or commercial planes and asking for the latest reports. Others called the Bonanza Air Lines, in Las Vegas, to inquire whether its Reno-bound flights, which would be halted by the C.A.A. when a shot was impending, were leaving on schedule. The movements of known scientists staying at Las Vegas hotels were carefully observed by bellhops and guests. "It got so that, besides worrying about gambling takes, we were worrying about our own skins," a hotel manager told me.

The members of the Atomic Energy Commission, being quite unconcerned about either the marriage-and-divorce business or the comings and goings of Nick the Greek, proceeded unhesitatingly with their project, convinced that they had chosen a site that was ideal for their purpose. To be sure, the Commission already had a proving ground at Eniwetok, out in the Pacific, but that was five thousand miles from its weapons headquarters, at Los Alamos, New Mexico. While the isolation Eniwetok affords was — and still is — considered advisable for the testing of certain bombs, the A.E.C. people felt that the majority of shots, to use the trade term, could be safely run off closer to home. Ralph Carlyle Smith, the Assistant Director of the Los Alamos Scientific Laboratory, enumerated for me some of the considerations that prompted them to establish the Nevada proving ground. "It's a terrible waste of valuable time to have our scientists spend all those days traveling to and from Eniwetok," he said. "Since the island is hardly within commuting distance of New Mexico, whenever they go there, they stay there — for six months or so, without their families or any of the amenities of life. And it's a nuisance to have to keep the island free of pests by continually spraying it from the air. Screens are useless there. The corrosion caused by that tropical climate is something fierce. I've seen buildings practically disintegrate before my eyes. Apart from all this, it's important for us to be near our laboratories, with their instruments. Some of the radioactive samples that have to be analyzed are extremely short-lived."

The Nevada site, which, as at least one of the blasts has proved, is within hearing distance of Los Alamos, had several things besides its handiness to recommend it, Smith went on. Consisting of six hundred and forty square miles of unpopulated land, it was looked upon as large enough to accommodate experiments with most kinds of atomic weapons. By the time radiation resulting from the explosions reached the nearest inhabited places, the A.E.C. figured, it would be sufficiently dissipated to cause no ill effects. (The A.E.C. also figured that if radiation in lethal strength *should* drift toward populated areas, there would be ample time to alert and evacuate the threatened citizens.) Furthermore, it was felt that delays caused by the weather would be fewer in the equable desert climate than in most other parts of the United States. Because rain tends to concentrate radiation, the desert's scant rainfall was regarded as an asset. So was the circumstance that strong winds, capable of carrying radioactive matter quickly to populated areas, are rare in this part of Nevada. And the almost daily clear blue skies over the desert would simplify the task of Air Force crews charged with precision bombing and with the tracking and sampling of atomic clouds. Moreover, the tract was already owned by the government (it had been bought during the war for an Air Force bombing range), so it would cost the Commission nothing. Finally, Las Vegas was considered both near enough to and far enough away from the proving ground — near enough for supplies to be delivered to the freight yards of the Union Pacific Railroad, on the town's outskirts, and for its population, of twenty-five thousand, to furnish the labor needed for constructing and maintaining the proving ground, and far enough away to insure the isolation required for reasons not only of safety but of security. "Out on the desert, anything that moves, animal or human, is an event," Smith said. "It can be seen for miles."

On January 26, 1951, the Commission let it be known that two nights earlier there had been a "dry run" to test the proving ground's communications and other facilities. At this point, the atmosphere of suspense in Las Vegas became almost unbearable, but it was dispelled at dawn the next day by an incredibly brilliant flash and, seven minutes later, a whacking blast that left a trail of broken glass from downtown Las Vegas clear out to the Strip. Operation Ranger — the name the A.E.C. gave its first series of tests — was under way. Most of the residents were awakened by tumbling window shades and shaking walls; some of them were tossed out of bed. Nobody was hurt, but one of the town's two daily newspapers, the *Review-Journal,* indulged its readers' dire expectations with the front-page headline "VEGANS ATOMIZED." All that day, there was worried speculation as to whether this might be only a tame curtain-raiser, but on the following morning a second shot came off and turned out to be no worse, and the atomized Vegans began to take their obstreperous neighbor in stride. Some of them expressed their relief by filing damage claims, of varying validity. Several homeowners declared that the shock waves had cracked the walls of their houses, but in more than one instance investigators found an accumulation of dust and cobwebs in the fissures. Others wanted reparations for broken water pipes, a few of which had obviously been corroding for years. The government was asked to provide new roofs to replace roofs that had been patched and repatched. A rancher in an area where no shock wave had struck charged that his chimney had been shaken loose and his house set on fire. A hermit living miles from town complained that his farm implements had been stolen "in the general excitement."

Operation Ranger consisted of five shots, which occurred on an average of one every forty-eight hours. Out along the Strip, the gamblers and divorcees took to throwing what became known as dawn parties — drinking and singing sessions that began after midnight and ended, if there was a shot that morning, with the sight of the flash or, if there was no shot, by just petering out around breakfast time. The Desert Inn's Sky Room, a glass-enclosed cocktail lounge with a sweeping panoramic view, was an especially popular spot for dawn parties. "It was a wonderful place for what the customers wanted," a waitress there told me. "They could sit around and listen to our piano player and look out the big windows and see the pretty hotel fountain and the guests swimming in the pool and the traffic speeding by on Highway 91, and then, just when they were starting to get tired, the A-bomb." The patrons at bars without views had to keep on their toes. As a bartender in one of these places recalled one afternoon, "Some fellow who'd been sitting around with his girl all night would suddenly look at his watch and say, 'Guess it's time for the bomb.' They'd grab their drinks and dash out, and then the rest of the crowd would follow them. After the damn thing went off, they'd all disappear, but by that time we'd have done more business than if we had television out here."

One night early in February, at the proving ground, Carroll L. Tyler, the Test Manager, and Dr. Graves, the Test Director, received a weather report from their meteorologists that led them to postpone a shot originally scheduled for the coming dawn. The two officials drove back to Las Vegas, arriving at their hotel — it was the Last Frontier, and they were well known there — at about three in the morning. Before turning in, they decided to breakfast in the hotel's Gay Nineties Bar, which was jammed with the usual dawn-party set. They had hardly sat down when they had the place to themselves and a hotel official was at their table pleading with them never to stop by there at that time again. "He said that we should have gone right upstairs and that he'd have been delighted to present us with breakfast in our rooms," Tyler recalls.

The townspeople didn't go in for dawn parties. They had less turbulent ways of greeting the unnatural daylight that was breaking spasmodically over their community. "Around five-thirty in the morning, the lights would start going on in my neighborhood," I was told by Doris Leighton, who is an administrative assistant at the Nevada Construction Company, a contracting firm. "Some of us would come out on our porches with cups of coffee and wait there. We'd be wearing heavy wrappers, because those winter mornings were quite nippy, you know. Sometimes husbands would back their cars out of the garage and into the street to get a better view. They'd let the motor run until the car was warm, and then their families would come out and join them. I used to see parents pinching small children and playing games with them to keep them awake. I guess they wanted to be sure their kids would see history in the making. People all looked expectant, but in different ways. Some, you could see, were afraid. Others smiled and acted non-chalant."

"There was one dawn test I saw from a rooftop, and I'll never forget it," Mrs. Donald Lukens, the wife of a Las Vegas journalist, told me. "When I could see again after the blinding, terrifying flash, I was looking at the sun. It was just coming up over the mountains. The sun, you know, isn't always kind to us here in the desert, but at that moment it seemed like an old friend. It made me feel safe."

Operation Ranger came to an end with a shot at dawn on February 6, 1951. The following October, the second series — Operation Buster-Jangle, seven shots — started up. During Operation Buster-Jangle, Las Vegans displayed little of their earlier skittishness. Less worried now about their own skins, they showed a tendency to regard the proving ground as a good thing. Many heads of families were holding down steady, well-paying jobs with the Commission, and, far from scaring visitors away, the experiments, and the resulting publicity, were actually attracting more. To the joy of the shopkeepers, many of the new visitors turned out to be of a different breed from the accustomed ones who passed up the town in favor of the Strip and spent their time and money out there. Now Las Vegas was besieged by people who cared little about room service and gambling; they bought their own groceries, and cooked them in trailers or motels. They were not interested in getting married or divorced; they simply wanted to be on hand for an explosion. When a detonation was in prospect (by this time the Commission was disclosing its plans), they got into their autos and, along with numbers of Las Vegans, headed for Mount Charleston, a forty-two-hundred-foot vantage point about fifty miles southeast of the test area. "Bumper to bumper, just like a ball game," an attendant at a gas station along the way said in describing the cavalcade.

Meanwhile, business at the big hotels was excellent, too. "I don't know exactly how much the bomb had to do with it, but around shot time the play in our casino seemed to go up and the drinking got heavier," I was told by Wilbur Clark, the head of the Desert Inn. "The curious thing was that guests would drive here from Los Angeles to see a shot and then not bother to look at it. I'd instruct my pitmen to let the players at their tables know when it was about time for the flash, but the players would go right on with their games."

A shot that took place on the morning of November 1st, sent Las Vegas its most jolting shock. Over two hundred damage claims were filed as a result — a record number at the time. "That was another time we had an especially good take on gambling," Clark recalled. "Same for liquor. Hell, I took an extra drink myself."

Most of the shots of the second series went off between 7 and 8 a.m., instead of at dawn, but that was no bar to dawn parties. One of the parties turned out to have nothing to celebrate, but everybody there had a fine time just the same. "That was quite a night," Ted Mossman, the pianist at the Sky Room, told me one evening. "Standing room only. They were drinking like fish. Some of them had cameras for photographing the flash — a thing they couldn't have done even if they'd been sober. It's too bright. Everyone wanted to sing. They requested all the old numbers — 'Margie,' 'The Sidewalks of New York,' 'Bye, Bye, Blackbird,' 'Put Your Arms Around Me, Honey.' They sang as if they were on the Queen Mary and it was going down — loud, desperate voices. After a while, I couldn't take it any more, so I improvised some boogie-woogie that I called 'The Atom-Bomb Bounce.' I kept playing it and playing it, until I thought my fingers would fall off. Seven o'clock in the morning, we get word there's been a circuit failure out at the proving ground and the bomb's called off. The crowd took the news fine. They all started betting when the next bomb would be exploded — the week, the day of the week, the hour of the day."

By no means everyone in Las Vegas and its environs has become resigned to the Commission's activities. Certainly no one can blame a rancher by the name of Carroll, whose water hole was found to be dangerously close to the test area, if he is inclined to bridle at the mere mention of the A.E.C. Carroll had already had to move his herds once, back in 1945, when the Manhattan District requisitioned his grazing land in New Mexico for the first atom-bomb test. When the authorities informed him he would have to move a second time, and why, it was almost too much for him. "Oh, Lord, no, not again!" he cried out as he grasped the significance of the deputation that had come to wait upon him. Some of the A.E.C.'s security guards turned cowhand for a day to help drive Carroll's cattle to a new range, but that did little to assuage the rancher's exasperation.

Among the other people who wish the government had located its proving ground elsewhere, some are convinced that a variety of melancholy events are attributable to the explosions. There is a tendency among people who have recently been afflicted with any disease to blame it on the bomb. Governor Charles Russell, of Nevada, told me that one Las Vegan had written to warn him that if the explosions weren't discontinued soon, the minds of southern Nevadans would be addled by the tremendous light and sound waves. The Governor also said that he knows of an old prospector who is living in perpetual dread lest his small outcropping be hit by a bomb. A woman in California has telephoned the Governor several times to express her conviction, in the face of his repeated denials, that federal prisoners are deliberately being exposed to the weapon's radiation, "like the mice and goats on Bikini." The experiments were widely regarded as responsible for the winter's abnormal severity in northern Nevada in 1952. During one particularly cold spell, nine manganese miners, whose work was being hampered by snow and ice, petitioned Governor Russell to put a stop to the detonations, and he, in turn, asked some meteorologists at the University of Nevada to look into the matter. They assured him that, far from being localized, the bad weather condition prevailed throughout Montana and the Dakotas, and, as far as they knew, had nothing to do with the bombs.

Still, the Governor said, every now and then, while reading his mail, he finds himself wondering who is right — the nuclear physicists or his correspondents. "The whole field of atomic energy is so new," he went on. "Perhaps the scientists will eventually come around to agreeing with the beliefs of some of the people who write to me. But no matter who's right, it's exciting to think that the submarginal land of the proving ground is furthering science and helping national defense," the Governor added. "We had long ago written off that terrain as wasteland, and today it's blooming with atoms."

After a third series of shots had come and gone, the predominant attitude in Las Vegas toward the proving ground was one of casualness. In fact, that series, which ended in June 1952, was generally dismissed as having been something of a dud. There were eight shots, and none of them gave the town more than a mild tremor. Only twenty-odd damage claims were filed. The townspeople didn't bother to climb up on their rooftops to sight billowing atomic clouds, and dawn parties went out of style. "Bigger bombs, that's what we're waiting for," said one night-club proprietor. "Americans have to have their kicks." The local A.E.C. offices, according to Marjorie Allen, a secretary there, received several complaints that the third series was a let-down. "After one of our shots, we got a phone call from a sweet old man who had heard about this grousing and was afraid we were taking it to heart," Miss Allen went on. "He just wanted to let us know that he'd been fishing out at Lake Mead at the time of the shot and that the shock wave had come in nice and strong there."

Many Las Vegans had become nostalgic connoisseurs, pining for the days of the unannounced, robust dawn shots of Operation Ranger. "Good bangs, and so pretty coming at sunrise like they did" is the way one veteran recalled the early tests. Others, less aesthetically inclined, fondly remembered the concussive quality of the November 1st shot. One day during the third series, Joe McClain, a columnist for the *Review-Journal,* which once had Las Vegans atomized, used his space to accuse the A.E.C. of "gypping its public."

> Time was when a nuclear detonation took place, people knew about it [McClain wrote] . . . People seemed to enjoy the show. But the good old days of Operation Ranger have passed. The scientists, to speak loosely, seem to have a little more control on the old fireball . . . Yesterday afternoon we had several calls wondering when "the A-bomb was going off." The people were real sore when they learned it already had been detonated. We think it might be good for the town's spirit if the scientists would send a few effects down Vegas way. Just to keep people happy.

At present, Las Vegas is a shrill, restless resort town. While this is as true when tests are not in progress as when they are, Chamber of Commerce officials and hotel people attribute the community's present condition in large part to the publicity that the proving ground has given it. "We're in the throes of acute prosperity," one hotel man informed me. "Before the proving ground, people just heard that this was a wide-open town. Now that we're next door to the atom bomb, they really believe it." The pangs of prosperity are especially perceptible to visitors try-

ing to book rooms in Strip hotels. Even when one of them is successful in making a reservation, his triumph may not last if the
degree of his gambling isn't sufficiently impressive. While I was
visiting Las Vegas, an acquaintance of mine who was staying at
one of the larger hotels was hailed by a desk clerk as he passed
through the lobby, and brusquely asked to give up his room. The
guest took the matter up with a managerial assistant, who simply
said, "We've got a ten-thousand-dollar player waiting for that
room. What do you think keeps the doors open?" The guest packed
up and left. At another hotel, an Eastern scientist, just arrived in
Las Vegas for the first time, felt that he was on the verge of landing a room when, spotting some crapshooters in the lobby, he
was reminded of a mathematical technique known in scientific circles as the Monte Carlo method and used by physicists to estimate the odds on such eventualities as a neutron's escaping from
a pile or causing fission. He started discoursing on this to the
desk clerk, whose face at once took on a bored expression. "I
informed him that I preferred gambling with the Monte Carlo
method, a rather ingenious form of nuclear craps," the scientist
told me later. "The next thing I knew, he was informing *me* that
he had a lot of mail to sort — and no rooms."

Some of the scientists, however, are on occasion quite willing
to indulge in the more conventional forms of gambling. The evening following a shot, when the strain under which they have
been working eases up for a while, they are likely to be far less
interested in computing nuclear odds by the Monte Carlo method
than in letting off steam by the accepted Las Vegas method. At
such times, a number of them are to be seen playing blackjack in
the casino of the Last Frontier. There they while away the evening
at the green baize tables, sipping highballs and chain-smoking.
They weigh the purchase of a card with as much concentration
as if they were pondering a problem in nucleonics, and become
too absorbed to take notice of the crowd around them — towns-

people who, having watched the hotel's night-club show for the price of a cup of coffee, are killing a few dollars at the slot machines; divorcees in long evening dresses, cheerfully rolling dice; shrewd-faced Hollywood figures at the roulette wheels; impecunious soldiers ordered to Nevada for atomic maneuvers, who play blackjack vicariously by staring at the cards in the gamblers' hands. Finally, soothed by the unpredictability of the cards, the scientists go off to their rooms. On such evenings, when the scientists are at the Last Frontier and it may be taken for granted that no atomic bomb will explode in the desolate wilderness to the northwest, Las Vegas, for all the heavy play at its tables, seems less of a gambling town than usual.

v

THE MAN

IN THE THICK LEAD SUIT

AFTER I LEFT NEVADA, I set out by train for Grand Junction, Colorado, to have a look at some of the uranium mining and prospecting operations on the Colorado Plateau. A short distance out of Salt Lake City, heavy spring floods held up the train and it fell fully five hours behind schedule. I spent a long, wakeful night aboard the coach without much else to do but think, and óne of the many things that crossed my mind was Dr. Graves's comment, soon after the atomic detonation I had witnessed, that, for all his knowledge of the exact pressure measurements of nuclear devices, he had to be vague about the fate of individuals and their homes in the event of war. The closest I had ever come to learning such information, I realized, was in the headquarters of the Office of Civil Defense Planning in the Pentagon Building, in Washington, three years or so before meeting Dr. Graves.

Ever since the last war ended, our military leaders had been saying that if war broke out again, our cities and towns could not escape enemy attack. The Secretary of Defense, consequently, had established the O.C.D.P., most of whose members were civilians, to study the problems and make some recommendations. After

eight months of research by the two hundred specialists assigned
to the office — engineers, psychologists, educators, doctors, lawyers, mass-evacuation experts, fire and police chiefs, chemical-
warfare officers, radiologists, and so on — the O.C.D.P. turned in
a report entitled "Civil Defense for National Security." It was
then carefully studied by ten federal agencies and departments,
including the National Security Resources Board, the National
Military Establishment, the Department of Agriculture, and the
Department of the Interior, which are charged with reducing the
hazards of enemy attack.

"Civil Defense for National Security," at the time, was undoubtedly the most elaborate study ever undertaken of the extent
and kind of damage a direct military attack on this country might
cause, and of how civilians could best protect themselves and
their property. The report ran to more than a hundred thousand
words. It went into such matters as the feeding of evacuees, the
detection of radioactivity, the removal of debris, and the setting
up of morgues. The men who prepared it — all of them well
known in their professions — were permitted to draw on a number of federal sources, such as the Atomic Energy Commission
and other agencies in a position to know how much punishment
this country could take. The findings of the United States Strategic
Bombing Survey, an Army and civilian unit that shortly before
the end of the last war investigated the damage our aircraft had
inflicted on enemy territories, were available to them. Also, British
civil-defense authorities provided information they gathered the
hard way during the Luftwaffe and buzz-bomb raids. Japanese
officials told what the American attacks had taught them. The
statements of survivors of the atomic bombings of Nagasaki and
Hiroshima were analyzed. Secret German documents on protective measures, which came into our possession fortuitously, were
studied. Hitler issued an order that they were not to fall into enemy
hands, but some of his civil-defense people dug up papers they

had buried and turned them over to Allied officers, explaining that they did so not out of affection for us but because they felt that such historic documents should be preserved.

A good deal of the material used in drawing up the report was gathered by Lieutenant Colonel Barnet W. Beers, the executive assistant of the Office of Civil Defense Planning, with whom I talked about the report in his office in the Pentagon. Colonel Beers, a thin, gray-haired reserve officer in his fifties, had been involved with civilian defense for eight years, which was longer than any of his colleagues and possibly longer than anyone else in the country. During 1945 and 1946, he headed a civilian-defense team attached to the Strategic Bombing Survey. This assignment took him to England, Germany, and Japan, where he found out as much as he could about what happens in a community while incendiaries and explosives are dropping on it. Before that, he was the Army's civilian-defense co-ordinator for the district that included New York, New Jersey, and Delaware. He also participated in the deliberations of the Army board that recommended establishing the Office of Civil Defense Planning. Colonel Beers said he was pleased that this unhappy subject was finally getting some attention. "It has always been the missing link in our military establishment," he told me. "Air, Navy, Army, and everything else have been getting built up, but not civilian defense. Isn't any war we fight supposed to be in defense of our homes? What this office is concerned with, of course, is passive defense. It won't knock out the enemy, but it'll keep *us* from being knocked out. And it's especially important now, with all these unconventional weapons and all the improvements on conventional ones."

I interrupted to ask him what he meant by "conventional" and "unconventional" weapons.

"Well, the rifle, the machine gun, artillery," he replied, "are conventional weapons — stuff we're accustomed to using. The atomic bomb is unconventional. So is biological warfare. This word 'conventional' we've fallen on is probably not very fortunate. Not so long ago, dropping a bomb on civilians was considered unconventional. Now it's called 'strategic bombing,' and accepted. As a matter of fact, this peace we've got on our hands strikes me as quite unconventional. I know it's popular today to claim that there can be no defense against nuclear weapons, but I consider that statement too broad. A defense has always been invented against every new weapon. Civilian-defense measures, for that matter, are a partial answer. Thousands of lives could have been saved at Nagasaki if the people who had been alerted had remained in their shelters, but somebody made a mistake and sounded the all-clear. People who didn't leave their shelters were unharmed, even those who were within a few hundred yards of zero, the point where the bomb went off. Of course, plenty of people in this country would get hurt by an atomic bomb, but we feel that we could cut down on the casualties. I look on civilian defense as a technique, almost a science. I know of many instances in the last war where it could have been better, but I don't know of any case where it didn't reduce losses."

There had been a good deal of spontaneous interest, entirely independent of Pentagon influence, in civilian-defense plans, Colonel Beers said. Citizens who were convinced that another war was impending had been badgering the government for several years to get on with a project. Michigan was still maintaining its wartime civilian-defense system. Chicago had a Disaster Relief Plan. Texas was particularly conscious of a need for civilian defense. "It started with the Texas City explosion," the Colonel said. "The Texans regarded that as a glimpse of what war might bring them. A lot of people in Maine had the same reaction after the Bar Harbor fire." Veterans who saw the destruction overseas wrote letters to the government demanding that something be done about home defense. Then, there were the civilian-defense workers themselves — the auxiliary firemen, the air-raid wardens, the ladies who learned first aid — who the Colonel suspected still recalled the stimulating days of blackout drills and staff meetings during World War II. A Philadelphian who had been a sector warden wrote the Army, "I am still standing by, ready at any time." He had moved to an apartment in a different neighborhood and wanted to find out whether or not he was still responsible for his old sector. An officer of a New York City organization called the Civilian Protection Schools Alumni had written to almost everyone in the Senate urging action. "His letters have been winding up on my desk," the Colonel said. A group of citizens in Superior, Wisconsin, had informed him that, pending instructions, its members were practicing on rifle ranges and conditioning themselves with calisthenics and long hikes. Sheriffs out West had sent word that they were ready at any moment to organize posses who might help.

Quantities of letters with ideas for improving defense were coming into the O.C.D.P. A Minneapolis resident thought that all men over forty ought to be drafted for civil defense. A Columbus, Ohio, woman suggested that civilians be required to carry maps indicating evacuation routes, hospitals, and first-aid stations. A New York engineer who had been through the San Francisco earthquake said that there should be a plan for the use of ferries and small harbor craft to help evacuate Manhattan. A high-school science teacher in Kansas felt that he and others in his profession should have data on radiological defense to include in their courses. "Here, look at this," the Colonel said, handing me a letter from a real-estate man in Lynn, Massachusetts, who wanted to know a good location for a "secondary residence" a client wanted to buy. A Midwestern schoolteacher who was going to spend her summer vacation looking for a lead mine she could hole up in when the bombs started falling asked whether an abandoned mine or one that was in operation would be better. A San Franciscan feared that a bomb might fall on the vault containing his safe-deposit box and make it radioactive.

The interest in defense planning manifested by these letters cheered Colonel Beers, but the naïveté of many of them was a constant reminder to him that most Americans had no idea what a bombing was like. "People have only their imaginations to go by," the Colonel said to me, "and they confuse scientific possibilities with operational probabilities. It's a scientific possibility that three people, lined up one behind another, can be killed by a single thirty-calibre bullet, but in war it takes thousands of rounds to kill one person. Things seem worse in our minds than they really are. If a raid came, we might be paralyzed by fear and do nothing about helping ourselves or anyone else or the local factory that's turning out war goods. The enemy would like to be able to count on panic. One conventional bomb in the right place at the right time might achieve for him the same psychological effect as a dozen atomic bombs. Look at how the Germans got the French to grab a canary and a blanketful of clothes, and clutter up the highways. You can't just tell people not to get panicky. It's a tricky proposition. You might even create panic by discussing it. Time, I suppose, is the big antidote for panic. If I knew that we were going to have another war in exactly twenty years, I'd say that next year was as important to civilian defense as the year of the attack. If people get used to the idea that they're supposed to do certain things under attack, they will take those things for granted. People go to Miami, although hurricanes are liable to hit that town, because they know that there are ways of protecting themselves and that they can depend on help from outside."

Our population might quickly adjust itself psychologically to enemy attacks, Colonel Beers told me, but physical preparations to protect it would take a lot of time, for they would be much more complex and numerous than those we had during the last war. "You simply don't know how powerful or novel a weapon the enemy may develop," Colonel Beers said. "The only way you can find out is to be hit with it. The Germans made a bad mistake in their civil-defense preparations. At the beginning of the war, their communal shelters were thick enough to withstand the heaviest bomb being made. Every time our bombs got heavier, the Germans had to look for more concrete. By the time the blockbusters were falling, there wasn't any more concrete, because their Army was using all of it for its own fortifications." Still, he said, certain assumptions have to be accepted, or nothing would get done. It is pretty safe to assume that fire would be the main hazard. Fire was by far the worst destroyer in World War II. In Hamburg, in a ten-day period during July 1943, a series of incendiary raids killed sixty thousand people.

"Hamburg had one of the worst firestorms in history," Colonel Beers said. "Five-alarmers are trifling compared to them." A firestorm starts when the air above the confluence of the columns of heat from a number of fires gets so hot that a violent updraft is created, as powerful as the strongest wind. The updraft of a firestorm heated to 1500° Fahrenheit moves at a hundred and twenty miles an hour. In Hamburg, firemen were sucked into the updraft. The cornices of buildings didn't fall, they floated away. Wet blankets that people had wrapped around themselves were torn off. Families in basement shelters suffocated, because the air was literally burned up. "Some people," Colonel Beers said, "have called these firestorms 'hurricanes of fire,' but even that is an understatement."

Colonel Beers paid his post-mortem visit to Hamburg in June 1945, and investigated the mistakes in civil-defense preparations that had been disclosed by the 1943 raids. "Hamburg might have had a different story to tell," he said clinically, "if the authorities had just anticipated the amount of firefighting equipment that would be needed in a war. Their fire mains were only as large as was necessary for normal times, and their water supply was inadequate. They had plenty of water right there in the Elbe, but why didn't they have enough pumpers for it? Their hose lines were too small and their water pressure was far too low. They were lucky to get two to three hundred gallons a minute through a hose. But that's no worry of ours. We've been able to pump a thousand gallons a minute in American cities for a long time."

Colonel Beers' findings in Hamburg were especially useful to the American fire chiefs who helped draw up the O.C.D.P. report. One recommendation was to station fire apparatus on the outskirts of cities instead of in the middle of them, where the equipment is more likely to be destroyed by bombings or fires. "It took the Axis two years to learn that," Colonel Beers said. "The same thing should be done with emergency stocks of food, fuel, clothing, and medicines. In Hamburg, the winter supplies of coke and coal were set afire by incendiaries and burned for weeks under a July sun. Another German mistake was the handling of reserves of firemen and police. Hanover would send two-thirds of its entire civil-defense force to help Hamburg. Then Hanover would get it, and Cologne men would have to be sent to Hanover. It was a terrible botch — people fighting fires in strange cities while their own homes were catching it." Radiological experts would have to be attached to fire departments, Colonel Beers said. "Otherwise," he explained, "a fireman might die trying to extinguish what he thought was a conventional blaze."

Any realistic planning in the last war, the Colonel went on, would have provided for a reserve of derricks, cranes, and steam shovels. The debris after a raid could be mountainous. "Many people who were in burning buildings would be alive today if the stuff hadn't blocked fire trucks," he said. On several occasions in Britain, where this equipment was in short supply, ten to fifteen thousand troops were diverted from their military duties to heave the masonry of collapsed structures manually out of streets and thoroughfares so that essential services could be resumed. Rescue workers, trying to get at people trapped underneath the rocky mess, had to work feverishly but carefully. "Their job was as ticklish as the disposal of unexploded bombs," Colonel Beers said. "They often had to work in a setting of live wires and sewer and illuminating gases."

All the emergencies that may face a city after a heavy bombing cannot be foreseen, of course, but by studying what happened during the last war the O.C.D.P. had been able to catalogue a staggering list of problems, ranging from the trivial to the enormous. The police, for instance, might be called upon to track down convicts who had escaped from shattered prisons at the moment that every man on the force was needed to deal with mobs of citizens who had turned to looting. "There's an odd compulsion to loot," Colonel Beers said. "I found out in Europe that even honest people can't resist the temptation to pilfer during a raid or just after one. Hysteria, I suppose."

The allocation of doctors and the providing of transport for them and other specialists, the commandeering of vans and trailers for ambulances (the one-patient ambulance now in general use is considered hopelessly inadequate for wartime needs), the quick removal of debris, the maintenance of sewage systems, the disposal of garbage, and the repairing of breaks in power lines and lines of communication are some of the problems that planning would simplify. The mass evacuation of civilians who have been bombed out is one of the trickiest jobs. "That's an awfully delicate time, right after a large-scale attack," Colonel Beers said. "That's when the public comes closest to, or is actually seized by, mass hysteria. The loss of relatives, friends, and property produces a profound shock. You have to counter this shock or public morale might simply collapse, which would be felt by our troops at the front. Immense quantities of clothing and rations would have to be kept on hand, along with the means of providing temporary shelter.

In a city as big as New York, schools, churches, libraries, and other public buildings would have to be utilized as billets or emergency hospitals. An information bureau where survivors could find out what had happened to their relatives is of major importance. In our report, we suggested that radio stations broadcast personal messages for separated persons. That would help morale no end, especially in New York, where there are so many commuters. I don't know why the Germans never did that. And casualty lists would have to be prepared as rapidly as possible. We think that the wearing of dog tags by civilians might be advisable. We also believe that it would be more humane to separate the morgues, instead of concentrating them in one district."

I inquired about defenses against atomic weapons, and Colonel Beers picked up his phone and asked Dr. Richard Gerstell to join us. "Might as well talk to the fellow who's been digging hardest at that," he said. "Gerstell was a lieutenant commander in the Navy on duty with the Manhattan District during the war and was a senior radiological monitor at Bikini. Had to inspect those hot ships." While we waited for Dr. Gerstell, the Colonel told me that the report his office had turned over to the Secretary of Defense estimated that each atomic bomb dropped on this country could cause an average of a hundred thousand casualties, forty thousand of them fatal. This calculation, he said, presumed the use of the Nagasaki type of bomb, the stronger of the two exploded over Japan. Like that bomb, this hypothetical one would be burst in the air, to cause the maximum destruction, but this one would be over an unalerted city. The fact that our building construction is generally more solid than that in Japan was taken into account, as was the density of population. The average American city of more than two hundred and fifty thousand population has between nine and ten thousand people per square mile; Japanese cities have between fifty and sixty thousand per square mile. "But

Manhattan has perhaps a hundred thousand people per square mile between 10 a.m. and 4 p.m.," Colonel Beers said. "New York is, however, unique. So is Los Angeles, at the other extreme — it's spread out over a tremendous area. We tried to strike an average."

Dr. Gerstell arrived, and turned out to be a young man with cropped hair and, considering the subject, a surprisingly jaunty way of talking. "Say this fellow flies in with his goddam bomb," he began. "Well, just about everybody within five hundred yards of where it explodes is dead as of right now. Radiation, blast, burns, structural collapse. From five hundred to a thousand yards, just about everybody in that area dead, too, but it might take three weeks for some. From a thousand to fifteen hundred yards, half of everybody dead, most of them not from radiation but from flash and flame. The next thousand yards, fifteen per cent. Five hundred yards beyond that, one to two per cent. Miles away, maybe from a cloud fall-out, a fission fragment hurts somebody, but unlikely. Shelters? You want my advice? Be somewhere else, sir, when a bomb goes off."

"Isn't there anything we can do about radiation?" I asked.

"Detect and avoid," Dr. Gerstell answered. "People in radioactive areas have to get out and everybody else has to stay out."

"Who's going to do the detecting?" I inquired.

"We'll have to train a lot of people to read Geiger counters, ionization chambers, and similar detection instruments. You can't feel, hear, see, or smell radiation. Twenty hours of teaching ought to enable a reasonably intelligent individual to use the equipment to detect it. It's not too hard to read the numbers on the dial of a survey meter, but the interpretation is something else again. You can tell with a thermometer that your uncle has a temperature of a hundred and one, but you still have to call in the doctor to find out whether he's really in trouble. Say your machine reads six roentgens for an area. You know that a tenth of a roentgen per twenty-four hours is considered to be the maximum permissible exposure. Well, a lot of people have to be evacuated from that area. Now, how long can each of your rescue workers stay in there? Here's the way you figure it. Six roentgens is sixty times your twenty-four-hour maximum permissible dose, so you divide twenty-four by sixty, and that gives you the answer — four-tenths of an hour, or twenty-four minutes. That's an extremely simple example. The interpreting gets complex when you have to evaluate the degree of contamination of food and water. The scientific boys have a lot of opinions about this, but when radioactive stuff is present, I bet they'll hesitate about putting in writing a statement that it's safe for people to drink this water or eat those onions."

"Haven't they developed some kind of protective clothing?" I asked.

"Ah, yes. The Neoprene cape," Dr. Gerstell said wryly. "Bunk. Your ordinary clothing will stop alphas, and maybe, if you happen to be wearing a thick lead suit, you'll make out all right against gammas and neutrons. After a raid, some personnel should wear masks — bulldozer drivers, say, who might rake up fission products while clearing away rubble. If your clothes are contaminated, take them off and bury them, and shower and shower until the fission products have disappeared from your skin. You can tell that by holding a Geiger counter against your body. Fission products have a cumulative effect. Actually, the chances of their hurting you are small, but why ask for it? Ideally, you don't want radiation of *any* sort. It wouldn't be a good idea to strap luminous-dial wristwatches all over your body and leave them there a couple of months. Why does the dentist make the patient use his own hand to hold the X-ray film in place in his mouth? The dentist doesn't like having his finger exposed to X-rays five or six times a day.

"Too much emphasis is being placed on radiation. The public's imagination is stirred up about it. In an aerial atomic bombing, ionizing radiation accounts for only fifteen per cent of the casualties. The rest are due to other causes — blast, falling buildings, that sort of thing. There might be certain situations in which we could help ourselves if we ever got hit with atomic weapons, but we wouldn't be able to if everyone thought he was an automatic goner after a raid. Panic — piling up in subways, shoving each other off the George Washington Bridge — can kill you just as surely as radiation. That can kill even the man in the thick lead suit."

Dr. Gerstell left, and Colonel Beers, possibly in a spirit of impartiality, next called in Lieutenant Colonel James McHugh to tell me about conventional weapons — chemical bombs, to be specific. They are generally nonexplosive, and they range in weight from a hundred pounds up to something over five hundred. They contain incendiary chemicals or poison gases compressed into liquid form. The simpler of the incendiaries burn out in a couple of minutes, but some of the contents of some of the gas bombs, especially mustard, lewisite, and chloropicrin gases, linger around for a long time. These bombs are vastly cheaper and easier to turn out than nuclear ones, and the Office of Civil Defense Planning felt that a lot more of them than of anything else would be used in an attack on this country. Colonel McHugh, a quiet-spoken man who had been with the Army's Chemical Corps eleven years, thought that an invader would most likely resort to gas. "An enemy, especially a have-not enemy — and that's the only kind we have — would want to come in and take over our factories and resources rather than win a shambles," the Colonel said. "This last war proved how phenomenally expensive an occupation can be if everything in the conquered nation has been banged up. But that's only my opinion, and we're certainly not overlooking the likelihood of attacks on facilities, too. If strategic installations were the targets, incendiaries at least as formidable as the ones our planes dumped on Hamburg and Tokyo could be expected. The defense is the fireproofing of buildings and the amplification of firefighting facilities. The only thing individuals can do is duck into shelters, which I hope will be gasproof."

In coping with gas, the civilian has to help himself, and training is imperative. Anyone with the training and the equipment can save himself from poison gas. If a man's trousers were splashed with liquid mustard gas, he'd be all right if he cut off the splashed part with his jackknife, washed off any of the liquid that had got on his skin, and applied a protective ointment — a tube of which he should have in his pocket — to the exposed areas. "These chemicals aren't like radiation," Colonel McHugh said. "A person covered with them can be decontaminated, but you have to work fast. You have only two to three minutes to avoid a burn, and your injury, like sunburn, may not show up until two to six hours later." Training to detect the characteristic odors of the various gases is necessary, so that they can be identified at the first whiff. After three or four whiffs, one becomes used to it and it's harder to detect, so a person might go on unsuspectingly breathing the stuff until he is beyond help. The eyes, the nose, the throat, the skin, and the respiratory system suffer the greatest damage. Gas masks and protective clothing are the best safeguards. One-piece hooded suits have been made up of an impermeable material that looks like oilcloth, and people wearing them and gas masks have spent long periods of time without injury in test chambers containing heavy concentrations of gas. There are certain secret protective preparations that can be used to impregnate clothing. "That woollen suit you've got on would do fine," Colonel McHugh told me. Cotton gloves can be impregnated easily, and there is a special compound that gasproofs shoes. In an emergency, dry cleaners and laundries could be equipped to impregnate clothes. "But the fellow with a big wardrobe couldn't send out his twenty suits," he added. "We're kind of short on impregnating materials. Maybe in the long run it would be more feasible to issue everybody standard gasproof overalls."

I asked Colonel McHugh if civilians could sleep in reasonable security in treated pajamas. "Pajamas are too thin," he answered. "To be safe, you'd have to keep on your protective clothing." He thought about that a moment, then said, "Hell, if we ever reach the point where everybody has to sleep in impregnated clothes, we'll be on the losing side. I don't believe that'll happen."

After Colonel McHugh had gone, Colonel Beers leafed through the thick report on "Civil Defense for National Security." "There's still biological warfare," he said, "but I'm not going to tell you about that. We're still quite secretive about it here in Washington. But I can get you some unrestricted stuff on the curious effects of the blast produced by high-explosive bombs. In Coventry — "

I told Colonel Beers I didn't think that would be necessary, and said that after listening to his experts I felt uneasy sitting in a fat target like the Pentagon Building. The Colonel smiled. "Not a very good example of dispersal," he said, "but I'm sure the military establishment has detailed plans for dispersing at the right time. Here in the defense-planning section, we've done a lot of thinking about dispersal, particularly for metropolitan dwellers. We are appalled by the sight of skyscrapers packed alongside each other, by the lack of open spaces, such as parks and playgrounds, that could serve as firebreaks, by the presence of key factories in heavily populated areas. However, dispersal, city planning, and all those matters are long-range propositions. We're worried about more immediate questions. Air-raid shelters, for one. Our report says they're unquestionably valuable, but it also says that the initial attack might come without warning and that in such a situation few people would get a chance to use them. Is it psychologically sound to lay out the materials and the manpower needed for shelters? To tear up Fifth Avenue so as to deepen and protect its sewer mains, water mains, and electric lines? Another problem is a standard aircraft-warning system. Should we have different signals for different kinds of raids? Is there a better warning sound than a wailing siren? You know, it scares some people more than is necessary."

Colonel Beers' office had also been trying to decide upon the value of blackouts and dimouts, which slow up production, increase traffic accidents, and in general disturb a community's life. Manuals were being prepared for fire chiefs and engineers, and a survey of urban water-supply systems was planned. Civil-defense people were to maintain liaison with the Research and Development Board of the National Military Establishment, so that they could be kept informed of new weapons against which new protective measures might be needed. There were the problems of improving instruments for the detection of radiation and gas contamination and of developing what Colonel Beers calls "an all-purpose mask" for civilians. Methods of preventing or quelling panic were being studied. "Plans, plans, plans," the Colonel said.

"Maybe there won't be another war," I remarked as I got up to go.

"That would be good news," the Colonel said. "I'd like it fine if there didn't ever have to be any civil defense anywhere in the whole world."

vi

THE COMING THING

WHILE THIS COUNTRY'S SUPPLY of nuclear weapons may be the largest in the world, the same cannot be said of its known deposits of uranium, that essential raw material from which the bombs, as well as more salutary applications of atomic energy, are manufactured. Indeed, a large part of the radioactive material that is going into our atomic piles comes from the Shinkolobwe mine in the Belgian Congo. Canada, thanks to extensive deposits at Great Bear Lake, in the Northwest Territories, is also providing us with many tons of uranium. Another of the world's important sources of uranium is the Erzgebirge region in Saxony and Czechoslovakia, but that, unfortunately for us, is under Soviet control. While our supplies are adequate at present, the Atomic Energy Commission has felt from the start that this country ought to develop its own uranium deposits with the utmost speed in order to make itself as little dependent as possible on foreign sources. Any number of unpleasant contingencies might disrupt the steady flow of ore from abroad; a Congo Mossadegh might emerge to make hash of our atomic planning, or Canada might expand its nuclear research to a point where it would feel justified in holding back the greater part of its uranium for its own use. And, of course, no one knows how the outbreak of another world war might affect our uranium imports.

Since 1948 the Commission, as a result of this edgy feeling, has been urging prospectors to make an exhaustive search for uranium here at home. By way of inducement, the government is paying a far better price for uranium than private industry did before the war, when uranium was used primarily for such amiable non-essential purposes as coloring pottery and tinting false teeth. (The Commission now strictly limits the amount of uranium that the nation's manufacturers may use for non-military purposes.) Mine-owners are being paid double for their first ten thousand pounds of uranium oxide — the chemical compound in terms of which the uranium content of the ore is assayed — to get them digging. These and similar incentives have started a uranium rush of some magnitude. Indians are roaming the desolate western canyons in search of rock formations bearing the yellow markings that indicate deposits; having spent their lives in this wild region and being free of preconceived ideas about geology, the Indians have proved particularly adept at finding uranium in unlikely rock formations. Veteran prospectors, who until recently were panning streams for gold, are now concentrating on uranium. Amateur prospectors have bought themselves Geiger counters and are taking to the hills in their spare time. (There are several models, each of which employs one or more of three ways of showing that its owner is on the right track — flashing lights, a dial indicator, and a clicking mechanism with earphones attached; the Super Sniffer, a $49.50 job turned out by the Nuclear Chemical & Instrument Corporation, in Chicago, is a popular beginners' model that both clicks and lights up.) It is not uncommon for families in some of the Western states, in which uranium seems to exist more abundantly than elsewhere, to take along their counters, together with their thermos bottles, when they set out for a day in the country. A year ago, an archeologically-minded North Dakota couple were looking for pictographs when their counter, which they had taken with them as a matter of routine, set up a feverish clicking that led them to a find that turned out to be far more rewarding, in a material sense, than any pictograph they may have missed in their excitement. An Arizona plumber underwent a comparable experience. After a luckless day of fishing in a small reservoir, he was trudging back to his car with his rod and his counter when, casually slipping on his earphones and flicking the switch, he, too, heard the rapid clicking. The next day, he returned to the spot with pick and shovel, started digging, and came upon an extensive deposit of uranium. A dentist in Grand Junction, Colorado, has learned that one way to distract patients whose teeth he is about to drill is to tell them how smoothly the drilling operations in a small uranium mine he owns across the state line in Utah are coming along.

While, thanks to the Commission's efforts, uranium is being discovered in a number of areas widely scattered throughout the country, the great bulk of what we are now mining domestically comes out of the Colorado Plateau — a region that has lured prospectors ever since the West was settled. The plateau, which has an area of a hundred and thirty thousand square miles, spreads out in all directions from the point where Colorado, Utah, Arizona, and New Mexico meet and includes some of the most rugged terrain in the United States — grim, seemingly limitless expanses of desert sand and forbidding ranges of sheer, snow-capped mountains, some of whose so far unscaled heights are tantalizingly believed to be studded with uranium. The plateau has its roads, but they are few, narrow, tortuous, and unpaved. It is for the most part a trackless as well as a waterless waste, and the living conditions of the men hacking away at its rocky fastnesses are exceedingly primitive.

It was Dr. Phillip L. Merritt, the assistant director for exploration of the Commission's Division of Raw Materials, which has offices in New York, who arranged for me to travel by car and rail through this geologist's dreamland, mostly in the company of a couple of notably well-informed officials, so that I could see how operations are progressing in our biggest uranium field. The starting point of my trip was to be Grand Junction, a town of fourteen thousand people, where the Commission maintains an operations office, and Dr. Merritt gave me the names of several geologists to look up there. Upon my arrival at the Grand Junction headquarters, situated in a two-story building near the Gunnison River, I asked my way of a man I encountered just inside the door, and found I was talking to one of them — Mike Reinhardt, a stocky, middle-aged fellow who is a Commission staff geologist. "We've been expecting you," he said. "Welcome to the great outdoors. I don't see how anyone lives in New York." As we walked down a corridor, he informed me that my guide for the first part of the trip, to the Navajo reservation in Arizona, would be Dr. Robert J. Wright, the assistant chief geologist; when we reached Indian country, I would be taken in tow by Jack Leonard, one of the Commission's liaison men with the Navajos. Reinhardt showed me into Wright's office, which was empty at the moment. We sat down to wait for Wright, and Reinhardt gave me some pointers about my forthcoming journey.

The first thing Reinhardt told me was that I shouldn't expect to find the uranium miners primarily motivated, as they toiled away, by any brightly burning concern over the international situation. "Uranium is strictly a living to them, and not an easy one, either," he said. The ore they mine, he went on, has to contain at least one-tenth of one per cent of uranium to qualify for purchase by the government; anything less requires too much processing to make it economically worth while. He pointed out that while many laymen are under the impression that there isn't much uranium in the world, that's far from being the case. It occurs in many common types of rock and, for that matter, in sea water and most drinking water, but generally in such minute quantities that the outlay for machinery and chemicals would not be justified.

Of course, Reinhardt continued, there are grades of ore far richer than those ordinarily found on the plateau. "A mineralized tree, now, there's a real find," he said. "I mean one in which geological processes have replaced the original vegetable tissues with uranium. The uranium content of such a tree sometimes runs to fifteen or twenty per cent. Two of them, I believe, once netted a miner a total of a quarter of a million dollars." These arboreal bonanzas, which are estimated to be around a hundred and twenty million years old, are the result of tremendous geological changes, Reinhardt explained. The first of these was the Triassic period, an arid era that lasted twenty million years. This was followed by the equally long Jurassic period, when the sea covered much of western North America, among other areas. Then, eighty million years ago, by the Laramide Revolution, perhaps the earth's greatest upheaval took place. It was the Laramide's violence, Reinhardt said, that molded the Andes and the Rockies and also twisted the Colorado Plateau into what he termed "its weird, contorted uplift."

By and large, Reinhardt added, the ore thus far discovered on the plateau hasn't been nearly as good as the ore we receive from the Belgian Congo. This is because the African uranium is found in veins — exceptionally rich ones, too — of pitchblende, a mineral that contains the element in a purer, more concentrated form than does carnotite, the mineral in which most of it is found in this country. Unlike pitchblende, which runs in narrow, more or less vertical veins, carnotite frequently spreads out horizontally on surface rock, or rimrock — a fact that has caused uranium prospecting on the plateau to become known colloquially as "walking the rim."

Suggesting that we look at some ore specimens, Reinhardt led me to a table at one end of Wright's office, on which was a collection of mineral fragments, along with a Geiger counter. Reinhardt handed me a small chunk of rough black rock, which, for its size, was extremely heavy. "From the Congo — pitchblende," he said. "As you can see, black as pitch, which accounts for its name." He took the pitchblende from me, hefted it fondly for a moment, and then gave me a piece of carnotite to hold. It was a bright mustard yellow, and much lighter in weight than the pitchblende. As I gripped it, a bit of it crumbled in my hand. "Carnotite's quite friable," Reinhardt said. "In the pure state, uranium is steel gray, but it always comes mixed up with one or more other metals — copper, silver, cobalt, nickel, lead, vanadium. Prospectors on the plateau used to go after carnotite for its vanadium, but now that the word's out that there's a good uranium market, the vanadium, important as it is, has become more or less incidental." He picked up the Geiger counter and switched it on, holding it close to the specimens on the table. The instrument flashed its tiny bulbs like an agitated pinball machine as it measured the amount of radiation of various ores. "Well, that's what it's all about," Reinhardt said, and switched the counter off.

The drive for uranium was coming along fairly well, Reinhardt told me as we resumed our seats. He said that he was not permitted to give out production figures but that the rate at present is several times what it was when the government's prospecting program was initiated in 1948. He had an idea that the rate would pick up even more as time went on and the prospectors got the hang of modern ways of searching for uranium. A few of the prospectors, he added, were successful professional men who had come to the plateau from big cities to escape civilization, and occasionally it took them a while to settle down to the job at hand. "They enjoy poking around on a mesa, where there's no one within ten miles and they haven't any appointments to keep or any other obligations," Reinhardt said. "That's one of the joys of prospecting, all right, but a bigger one is finding something, and usually it doesn't take them long to realize that." He went on to say that prospectors of the old school seem to have as hard a time as they have traditionally had in holding on to the money they earn, and told me about one old-timer who had recently got hold of six hundred dollars. Returning in his jalopy to his home town, a plateau settlement with a population of fifty, where he owed money to half the inhabitants, the prospector got out, hailed a youngster, handed him the six hundred dollars, and told him to trail him down the middle of the town's one street. In each doorway stood a highly vocal creditor, and at each dunning the prospector would call grandly over his shoulder "Pay the man!" and the lad would peel off the proper number of bills. By the time that brief stroll was over, the old-timer had hardly enough money left to buy a drink.

Reinhardt said he thought his own contingent of geologists was setting a good example for the independent prospectors. There were thirty-nine of these geologists, many just out of college, swarming all over the plateau, and they represented a new kind of prospector, versed in geology and skilled in the use of technical equipment. "They never make a move without a Geiger counter," Reinhardt said. "One of those counters weighs fifteen pounds in the morning and feels like a ton by nightfall, and there are still some prospectors who won't use them. They consider them new-fangled contraptions, and just look for the color of the rock, as they did when they went after copper and so on in the old days." Most of his geologists have made at least one strike, Reinhardt said, but for them it's all in the day's work. Their job is to scout for areas that look promising enough to be investigated further. They're what might be called prospectors' prospectors. They receive no extra pay for their discoveries and no royalties on whatever uranium is extracted from their finds. Whenever preliminary drilling on a site of theirs indicates that it is worth developing, the government leases the prospective mine to a private operator.

So far, Reinhardt said, the cost of the drilling has been offset by the money the government has received for the leases.

The Commission's geologists do some of their prospecting in light planes equipped with extremely sensitive counters. (No radium paint is used on the dials of the planes' instruments lest the counters be led astray.) The planes skim the mountainsides, and whenever one of their counters detects radiation, a geologist accompanying the pilot bombs the spot with bags of flour to mark it for the scouting parties who will later approach it on foot. Most of the prospecting, however, is done by jeep or on horseback. Reinhardt was pleased with the way the young geologists have adapted themselves to the rigors of life on the plateau. "That's something that has little to do with a college degree," he said. "The majority of them have been used to soft living at home and in Ivy League schools. They may have majored in geology at college, but until they get here their knowledge of it is pretty theoretical. Fortunately, their interest in the subject seems to keep them going during those first few tough months out on the plateau, when survival rather than exploration is their chief worry." The country is so treacherous, Reinhardt said, that he insists his geologists always work in pairs. That turned out to be a well-founded precaution on at least one occasion, when a young Yale man, who had only recently arrived on the scene, fell off a ledge and started to roll down a rocky slope toward a sheer precipice. His partner, a University of California graduate, was standing a few feet from him, and grabbed him just in time.

"They soon catch on," Reinhardt continued, with some pride. "Before long, they're covering fifteen miles a day in deep-canyon country and snaking jeeps out of quicksand with no more trouble than they used to have changing a tire. They tramp through country where it's pretty certain no white man has ever been before and probably very few Indians. Still, you never can be sure. Every now and then, just when a couple of our boys are patting each other on the back and telling themselves that they're the first human beings ever to reach some all but inaccessible spot, they come on the name 'Wetherill' scratched on a rock, and that really takes the wind out of their sails." He went on to explain that during the latter part of the nineteenth century and the early years of this one there were four Wetherill brothers — Richard, John, Alfred, and Clayton — who spent a good deal of their time scouting for Indian ruins on the Colorado Plateau and who had a habit, disconcerting to latter-day would-be pioneers, of leaving behind incontestable evidence of their wanderings. "It's a letdown for our fellows," Reinhardt said. "They get all the way into the worst kind of remote country and what do they find? A message from one of Kilroy's predecessors."

Reinhardt was embarking on a philosophic soliloquy about how New Yorkers would benefit in body and soul if they moved West and started looking for uranium when Dr. Wright entered the office. He is a youthful, prematurely bald Ohioan, who was formerly an assistant professor of geology at St. Lawrence University, in Canton, New York. He seemed harried and distracted, and after quickly arranging to pick me up next morning at my hotel, he turned to a pile of correspondence on his desk. "Paper work, paper work!" he said grimly. "Geologists were never meant to be indoors."

When I climbed into Wright's Ford sedan the following morning, I found him a changed man. "Nice to be getting out of this headquarters town," he said jovially, stepping on the accelerator. "We probably won't be stopping anywhere for lunch, so I brought along a few sandwiches. Better have a last look at the metropolis. You won't see anything like it for the next few days." Presently, as he guided the car up a spiraling road into wild, mountainous country, he began exuberantly greeting each geological formation we passed as if it were an old friend. "The Morrison Salt Wash!"

he exclaimed as an eroded mass of rock, perhaps a thousand feet high, came into view. "That's a sedimentary Jurassic rock." Twenty minutes later, after we swung around a hairpin turn, Wright delightedly introduced me to the Brushy Basin, a sloping series of mudstone ledges. Then the sight of another geological masterpiece filled him with such pleasure that he stopped the car for two or three minutes to contemplate it. This was a manifestation of the Dakota Formation, which is a hundred million years old.

After his joy at being outdoors again had subsided, Wright, settling down to the grind of negotiating the rough, serpentine road, outlined my itinerary. I would be proceeding in a general southwesterly direction, he said, and the trip, which would take four days, would enable me to have a look at the two principal types of uranium areas on the plateau. One was the old-established mining region, where metals of various kinds had been dug out of the ground for over a century; we were traveling through that country now. The other was the region where the Indians were making their uranium finds, most of it in Arizona, but some of it extending well into New Mexico, as far as the town of Grants, which, Wright said, would be my last stop. At Grants, I would meet Paddy Martinez, a part-Mexican, part-Navajo sheepherder who had astounded geologists by discovering a tremendous uranium deposit in a limestone formation called the Todilto, on Haystack Mountain, twenty miles west of the town. "We were taught at school that uranium was extremely unlikely to occur in sedimentary rock of the limestone type, like the Todilto," Wright said. "I'm glad Paddy didn't take the same courses. The Indians have gone looking for carnotite figuring they might find it anywhere, and they've proved to be the program's secret weapon." He went on to say that Jack Leonard, who was to be my guide for part of the second half of the journey, had a downright gift for getting the Navajos interested in prospecting. "I wish I could drive on to Grants myself," Wright told me. "But there's always that paper work waiting for me back in Grand Junction. Anyway, I'll have a couple of days away from the office."

Three hours out of Grand Junction, we came upon the first settlement along our route — a pretty hamlet called Gateway, which has a population of sixty-five and lies in a canyon beside a small stream. Here was also the first water of any consequence we had encountered. Stands of poplar and cottonwood trees surrounded the village — signs of fertility that were almost startling after the stark, treeless country through which we had been driving all morning.

In a matter of seconds, we had passed through Gateway and were back in the mute wilderness of the plateau. After a few miles, we came to a steep downgrade where the road seemed to me to get much narrower, but that impression may very well have been caused by the fact that pressing in on Wright's side was an enormous, wall-like mountain and on my side, with perhaps two feet to spare, was the edge of a cliff that dropped precipitously several hundred feet to the silvery surface of a turbulent river. For ten minutes, Wright drove on gingerly, his jaws tense and his arms rigid, and then the mountains fell back on one side and the cliff on the other, and no parkway ever looked as gratifyingly broad to me as our road did at that moment. The mountains on either side of us now loomed taller and had sharper contours than the ones we had been driving through earlier. Wright, whenever he could, scanned them attentively. "There's a mine!" he said at last. "That's what I've been looking for." He slowed the car to a crawl and pointed out a small, blackish indentation near a dirty-white summit some five hundred feet above us. "It's impossible to tell from this distance whether there's anybody working up there," he went on. "All I hope is that they're not ten-day miners — men who quit after ten days or so and don't come back again till they've spent their money. Some of them do that in the privately owned mines. With those who are leasing from the government, of course, it's a different matter." Wright gave the mine another look and shook his head. "I still find it hard to believe that those measly black spots have anything to do with atomic bombs," he said. "Why, most of them are hardly any bigger than gopher holes, and usually no more than two to six men are needed to work them. Maybe a couple of hundred of them in all, on the whole plateau, with funny names like Buzzards' Roost and I Don't Know and Main Street. And that's the whole extent of one of the most important mining operations in the world! Oh, well, you never can tell how you'll get your uranium." As the car gathered speed, he added, "Did you ever know that the ore that made our first bombs possible came out of a Staten Island warehouse? It was stored there by a Belgian, a man named Edgar Sengier, who was the managing director of the Katanga mines in the Congo. Sengier didn't have anything specific in mind when he stored it there — certainly not the bomb. He was simply playing a hunch. He figured the Nazis would overrun Europe, so he shipped several tons of pitchblende to the United States, just on the chance that it might come in handy in some way or other against the Germans. The stuff lay there on Staten Island from 1940 until 1943, when the Manhattan District people, who were badly in need of it, heard about it and got hold of it. Sengier was awarded a Medal of Merit for his hunch. I guess it was one of the real breaks of the war."

Two hours out of Gateway, driving smoothly along on high ground, we looked down on the mill town of Uravan, which is owned by the United States Vanadium Company and is bisected by the San Miguel River, a stream that is rusty from the mine refuse that has been dumped into it for decades. The mill, the town's reason for being, was perched astride a hill, and we could hear crushed ore tumbling down an enclosed chute to the drying ovens. In the years just after the war, Wright said, Uravan had been well on the way to becoming a ghost town, because there were few orders for either of the products — uranium and vanadium — for which it was named, but then the government's intensified search for domestic uranium brought it prosperity. Now it is a purposeful-looking, if drab, community. "Population eight hundred, three telephones," Wright said. "One's in the general store, another's in the company's office, and the third's in the superintendent's home."

We turned in to a narrow side road to search for more gopher holes. After an hour, during which we ate our sandwiches as we drove, we had located two, but no one was around at either. "Guess they've made enough money for this month," Wright said irritably. A few minutes before four o'clock, which is quitting time in most of the mines, we arrived at one called Reserve Block 1. As soon as we got out of the car, a middle-aged derelict emerged from a make-shift shack and came shuffling toward us. "Living like a stinking coyote in this goddam country," he said. "I've worked as long as seventeen days in my time. I ain't no lousy ten-day miner." He turned in the direction of two men in their forties, who were standing some distance away in a welter of jackhammer drills, with an air compressor and a box of dynamite on one side of them and a narrow-gauge track supporting a small mine car on the other. "People!" he yelled to the pair, announcing us.

We approached the two men, the derelict trailing us valiantly. They were brothers, Cecil and Phil Bunker, to whom Reserve Block 1 had been leased by the Commission. Cecil, an earnest-looking man wearing a battered fedora, courteously said that he would have liked to show us through the mine but that we had arrived too late. Six men worked there, he explained, but the others had left for the day and he and his brother, following standard procedure at closing time, had just set off a charge of dynamite inside the shaft, creating fumes that would suffocate anybody who tried to enter. Their mine was producing nicely, he said, and he and Phil considered themselves lucky to be operating it; the Commission not only had discovered the mine but had given him and his brother a fair idea of how extensive the deposit was. "We should be busy here for maybe another couple of years," he said. "That's the kind of information it's darned valuable to have when you're mining uranium, because it's different from other kinds of mining. Sometimes when you're prospecting for uranium, you come across an outcrop that runs along for half a mile and you think you've got a real strike, but then you find there's nothing back of that yellow rim, and it's mined out in no time. It's a whole lot different from coal mining. Phil and I used to mine coal back home in Wilkes-Barre twenty years ago. We left there during the depression."

"Living like a stinking coyote," the derelict said again.

"He's our watchman," Cecil said in an apologetic tone.

"This is paradise compared to the way the miners are living in the back country," Phil said sternly, his eyes on the watchman. "Those guys are nowhere near towns the size of Uravan. They've got no machinery, like us — just wheelbarrows. And no beds — just sleeping bags." The watchman subsided, and Phil went on to say that another thing he and his brother liked about the uranium setup was the way the government guaranteed prices. "Now, lead, for instance," he began. He glanced at Cecil, and the two men laughed derisively. "Mining lead's like playing the stock market, the prices fluctuate so," Phil explained. "Then there's gold. Sure, gold's still pegged at thirty-five dollars an ounce, but, considering how costs have gone up and how hard it is to find the stuff, I'd say the price is pegged too low. We prospected for gold for years up around Victor, Colorado. No doubt about it, uranium's a much better deal nowadays. I guess the government won't ever get as much ore as it wants."

"I expect very few people know how much the government wants," Cecil said. "But they do say that this atomic energy is the coming thing."

"That's what we've heard," Phil said. "That's what makes me think we did right in quitting gold for uranium."

After we were back on the main road, Wright looked at his watch and said we'd have to keep driving steadily if we were to reach our first stopover point in time for a decent night's rest. That was Monticello, Utah, four hours away; there were no nearer overnight accommodations, he said. Halfway to Monticello, however, he relented when, thirsty and tired, we came upon a ramshackle store standing all alone on the edge of an immense plain. We went in and ordered Cokes. As we raised our bottles, the storekeeper, a beady-eyed middle-aged man, said to Wright, whom he obviously knew, "You want to see something?" Wright nodded, and the storekeeper went out back and returned with a jar of bright-yellow carnotite fragments, which he asked Wright to examine.

"They look pretty good," Wright said tentatively.

The storekeeper was delighted. "Darn right they do!" he said. "And there's plenty more where they came from. Man, this yellow runs on and on, and there's plenty back of the rim, too! I had a rough ride up the mountains in my jeep before I spotted it. But I'm not telling anyone else about it, leastwise after what happened a month ago." He gave us a conspiratorial smile. "A couple of fellows came into the store then for Cokes — just like you — and I showed them the jar," he continued. "They said they were oilmen from Oklahoma and they'd be back after they finished some business. I didn't tell them too much about where I found this stuff, but I figured they might be trying to get in ahead of me, so I went and posted a claim notice. I'm looking for a big boy who's not afraid to take a chance. I'll give him the land and take twenty per cent of the profits for myself, and I'm to be the manager and superintendent for five hundred a month. I've got something good, as sure as atomic energy is the coming thing."

As we drove away, Wright told me that the specimens looked promising but that he was skeptical about them because this part of the countryside had already been pretty thoroughly explored. "Good specimens are easy to come by on the plateau," he said. "People in these parts pass them around as souvenirs. Of course, if that fellow has really got something, the government would be glad to help him develop it, but I gather from talks I've had with him before that he doesn't want things that way and we can't force him to lead us to his find. What will happen, if he's not just enjoying a pipe dream, is that pretty soon this big boy of his will come back, or another one will show up, and put up the money. Then they'll start producing uranium ore, we'll start buying it, and everyone will be happy. Oh, well — anyway, we had our Cokes."

Now, far off in the distance, and for the rest of the waning day's journey, the jagged, snowy peaks of the La Sal Mountains, the tallest range we had yet seen, formed our vista. A blue haze lay over their ridges, a number of them more than twelve thousand feet high, and there was something vaguely inviting about them after the barren slopes that had flanked our route. At ten o'clock that night, the lights of Monticello shone below us, and Wright hurried the car downhill. When we reached level ground, we were on Highway 160, a paved road. "Feels slippery, doesn't it, after what we've been driving on all day?" Wright said. "Well, here's our motel. Now for a bath."

Wright and I had only one objective the following day — to reach the Navajo trading post at Kayenta, Arizona, where I was to meet Leonard — but we were on the road early, and had time to make a short, unscheduled detour to a uranium mine operated by the Vanadium Corporation of America. This was a larger mine than Reserve Block 1, and looked out across a wide, swift-running stream toward some cliff-dwellers' ruins. Horses hitched to steel carts were being led into the mine entrance — a hole in the side of a mountain — and they came out again tugging loads of ore, which were transferred to trucks. From within the mine came the faint but industrious chatter of rock drills. The foreman, an alert-looking young man named Calvin Black, invited us to follow him inside. "We're finishing a mineralized tree," he said. "It's only three hundred feet in." He handed us helmets equipped with carbide lamps and told us to stick close behind him. The instant we passed the mouth of the mine, we were in a world of darkness. As my eyes became adjusted to it, I could make out several long, low-ceilinged corridors. Miners, their slanting silhouettes etched against the walls by their flickering lamps, pressed at the ends of the corridors with jackhammers whose din ricocheted through the passageways — an almost tangible sound.

Black led us down a corridor in which I could see no drillers, although, as we picked our way over its soft, uneven floor, I could hear the persistent noise of a jackhammer, coming from directly ahead and growing steadily louder. That, Black told us, was where the tree was being worked on. "We're drilling it from the opposite side," he said. "You can hear the drilling, all right, but you won't see any." When we reached the tree, Black detached the lamp from his helmet and held it close to the wall of the shaft. "There she is!" he shouted, above the racket of the jackhammer. The contours of the tree, which was horizontal, stood out plainly against the inky surface of the rest of the wall; a dirty yellow, it was about fifteen feet long and a foot wide. At the end where the tree's roots had been, the yellow ore spread out into several mottled strands. "She's a beauty!" Black shouted. "Sixty feet long when we found her!" Wright, peering through the gloom, nodded approvingly. Suddenly, the drill ceased its furious jabbing in the corridor beyond, and in the new stillness Black said, "I guess that means Pete's gone to lunch."

"If that tree had been growing annual rings all these years, there'd be ninety million of them," Wright said. "Dinosaurs probably nibbled off that tree."

I asked what kind of tree it had been. "It probably looked something like a palm," Wright replied. "It had no branches, and its leaves grew directly out of the top of its trunk — like a bouquet in a vase."

"Sure wish I owned her," Black said respectfully as we started making our way back to daylight. "She drives a Geiger counter wild. I'll bet we get six tons or more of really high-grade ore out of her."

Outside again, Black told us that once, while out prospecting, he had found a mineralized tree and cleared eighteen hundred dollars on it for only a few hours of labor. "Maybe I own a tree right now," he added. "I have six claims, but there's one in particular, about forty-five miles from my home town — Blanding, Utah — that I consider really promising. I haven't developed it yet, but I'm thinking about it pretty hard. I've got a good job here, but that tree we just looked at has made me a little restless. Uranium is all I've bothered with since I left high school five years ago, and I guess I've been lucky so far. I own ten thousand dollars' worth of mining equipment and a third interest in the Blanding Electric Company." He glanced at some of his fellow-miners who were eating lunch fifty feet away, on a ledge of rock. "Maybe they're restless, too," he said. "Every one of them has at least one claim somewhere. Come on over and say hello."

Black led us to the group and introduced me as a visitor from New York. "Say, you got any hot information on how to get rich mining?" a burly, sandy-haired miner asked me. The others roared with laughter.

"Feed your kids and keep your clothes on, that's all you can expect," a skinny, handsome man told him. "This mine's the end of the world."

"I've got two claims that I don't know what to do with," another man said. "I can't afford the equipment to develop them and I hate to sell out to the big companies and watch them clean up. There's no such thing as an independent miner."

"It ain't the companies," one of the others put in. "The government ought to pay better prices."

"All this damn griping!" said an older man, sitting off by himself. "Everybody knows mining's all we'll ever do the rest of our lives."

The remainder of the day's trip was uneventful. We soon passed through the Mormon village of Bluff, and after that for a while a desert spread out before us like a vast sandy beach, except that it was dotted here and there by the clustered leaves of yucca plants. A few miles farther on, there was a short stretch of Navajo sandstone — a prettily scalloped, reddish-brown rock, worn smooth by the winds. Still farther on, we saw a waterless river course that wound gracefully in and out among the bases of mesas that had been marvelously whorled by thousands of years of erosion. At about this point, we passed a sign, planted in the sand, that read, "DO NOT DUMP GARBAGE HERE."

Arriving in Kayenta late that night, we found that Leonard had already turned in and had left word with the proprietor of the trading post there that he'd like me to meet him at his jeep station wagon out back at six-thirty the following morning. "Jack's car has two coyote tails hanging from the radiator cap," the proprietor said. "You can't miss it." I told Wright as we walked to our rooms that there was no need for him to get up that early, and that I would introduce myself to Leonard. Then I thanked him for all he had done for me, and we said good night and goodbye.

Even at six-thirty in the morning, I found it easy to like Leonard. An amiable, quiet-spoken, blue-eyed man of nearly forty, he had an unmistakable air of reliability about him that at once commanded respect. It was his reliability, in fact, that had necessitated our getting under way at such an early hour. As we set out in the jeep, Leonard explained that two Navajos, a father and son, were expecting him that morning at their home near Cameron, three hours away. They had a find for him to inspect, and he hadn't felt it wise to change the hour of the appointment. "If you give them reason to believe that you don't keep your word, they'll ignore you forever," Leonard told me. "That's because they've been rooked so often on the sale of their sheep's wool, silver jewelry, and rugs. Nobody likes to be rooked, but the average Navajo family — and that's usually seven or eight people — lives on about four hundred dollars a year, so a little rooking means a lot to them. Just let a small misunderstanding grow up between the Navajos and us and our whole prospecting program might be hamstrung in two weeks. That's about the length of time it takes for the word to be passed from one end of the reservation to the other." Of course, he went on, the geologists would still be out searching for uranium, but their knowledge of the reservation, which covers about twenty-five thousand square miles, didn't compare with that of the Navajos, for these Indians are nomadic by nature, and many of them travel from one region to another, following the seasons, in search of good grazing conditions for their sheep and horses. "Under the circumstances, it would be pretty hard for them *not* to get to know the country," Leonard added.

Luckily, Leonard said, the Navajos have been co-operating with the government. In 1951, at the outset of the program to enlist their aid, it was by no means a certainty that they would co-operate, for the government's Indian policies haven't always been acceptable to the Navajos, among other tribes. "The only way we could prove our sincerity was to pay well and treat them squarely," Leonard told me. He said that in the beginning he had driven his jeep up and down and back and forth over the reservation, spreading the news among the sixty-five thousand Navajos about what the Commission was planning to do. Using trading posts as headquarters, he had signed up a number of dependable-looking Navajos and sent them out into the field, paying them a dollar and twenty cents an hour and encouraging them to try to interest their fellow-tribesmen in the undertaking. If they, or any of their unsalaried companions, found anything worth developing, he assured them, they would enjoy the same benefits from it as the other prospectors, who may also explore the reservation, provided they get permission from the Bureau of Indian Affairs. "At the start, we counted heavily on the hired Navajo prospectors to set an example for their fellow-tribesmen," Leonard said. "They had the incentive of their hourly wage, and we figured that when we paid them their money, just as we'd promised, the others would see that we were on the level." Leonard had known it would be useless to try to get the Indians to use Geiger counters, so he had left samples of uranium ore at each trading post. "I'd tell them to bring in rock like the samples, and that I'd be back in two weeks to see how they'd made out," he went on. "Then I'd shove off for the next trading post, wondering if anyone had given a damn about what I'd said."

Leonard had been astonished at the results when he made his second round of the trading posts. "The word had certainly gone out," he said. "At each post, there'd be twenty or more Indians waiting for me with samples they'd found. The Navajos aren't prospectors by tradition, but they have remarkable memories and powers of observation. They'd studied the specimens I'd left behind and then gone straight to canyons and mesas where, over the years, as they moved about with their herds, they'd come across the yellow of uranium. In some cases, it had been more than twenty-five years since they'd last seen those deposits, but they hadn't forgotten them, or how to get to them. Not all of them were so co-operative, naturally. At one of the posts, I heard about a Navajo in the Carrizo Mountains who had been eating bits of uranium as a medicine most of his life. I looked him up, but he was no help. He said that the other Navajos could find uranium for me if they felt like it, but that he was content to watch his sheep and let his young wife take care of him. His medicine may not have helped him, but it certainly hadn't hurt him. He was ninety."

A gratifyingly high percentage of the finds reported by his Indian prospectors had paid off, Leonard said, and the Navajos are still bringing in specimens that warrant investigation by the Commission's geologists. One of the prospectors, Alfred Miles, has tipped the Commission off to an area that, according to Leonard, may prove to be just about the richest strike on the whole plateau. "To look at Alfred, you'd never think he had it in him," Leonard said. "He's a little old dried-up fellow of fifty-two, but he runs me to death out on those trails. He and I were two days on horseback getting to his big discovery. It would probably have taken our geologists ten years to spot the place. It was on a crazy mountain, all cut up and no pattern to it at all. When we got there, we scrambled over endless tricky ledges, a good deal of the time on all fours. We hadn't even bothered tying our horses when we left them. Hell, they didn't want to wander around and fall into a fifteen-hundred-foot canyon. We kept running into wonderful showings, one of them four feet wide. They'll start mining there as soon as a road is completed."

By now, Leonard said, the Commission's geologists have enough showings on file to keep them busy investigating for years to come, and his own job is beginning to become routine. "I just look at samples or sometimes, like this morning, at an outcrop," he told me. "If it's worth while, I let the geologists know about it. The main thing now is to keep the Navajos convinced that they're getting a square deal, which they are." I asked him if the Indians understood what all the commotion was about. "Well," he said, "some of them think the government is just collecting rocks. They tell me I ought to want red rocks, not yellow, because the red is easier to find and softer to dig. Others think it's *ola* — gold — because the ore is yellow. Most of them, though, connect our program with some kind of explosive. They ask me if it's like a gun and I say that it's more like blasting powder — that it could blast out rocks for miles around. They have their doubts about that, so then I try to describe a bomb — just any old bomb — but even that's a difficult idea for them to grasp. Of course, it's a whole lot easier with the Navajos who were in the last war. They know what an ordinary bomb is like. I tell them it's bigger than anything they saw in the Army and let it go at that."

The road to Cameron was smooth, and although the day was windless, we were moving along at a clip that made the coyote tails flap wildly on the radiator cap. Leonard looked at his watch. "We'll be all right," he said, and slowed down long enough to light a cigarette. I mentioned that Wright had told me Leonard had had a lot to do with the success of the program on the reservation. If that was so, Leonard replied, it was probably because he could speak Navajo. Very few white men can, for it is an extraordinarily difficult language. "During the war," he said, "I was in a Marine outfit with some Navajos in the South Pacific and we found that the language made an ideal unbreakable code." I learned that Leonard had been raised in the Southwest and had picked up Navajo by spending a great deal of time with members of the tribe; his home, where he lives with his wife and three sons, is in Farmington, New Mexico, where he formerly owned a trading post. His present job doesn't pay very well, he said, but, apart from that, he finds it extremely agreeable. "What I really like to see is the way the Navajos are gaining prestige all over the country because of their contribution to our uranium program," he said. "Maybe if Alfred and the others keep scrambling, the powers that be will let them have a few more hospitals and schools."

Toward midmorning, Leonard swung the jeep off the road and up on a hillock, where he parked it a few yards away from a Navajo hogan — a circular house built of adobe and logs. This was the home of the two prospectors he had promised to visit. The father, a wizened fellow named Charles Huskon, came out to greet us, and behind him I could see the building's one, communal room. It was windowless, and a wood fire, on which food was being cooked, was burning on its dirt floor, making the place quite smoky. Huskon was followed by his son Evans, a flabby-faced youth in his twenties. Another Huskon, a lad of nine or ten, romped up to us from the fields and said something in Navajo to Leonard, who replied by wiggling his ears. The boy was delighted. Charles Huskon informed me, in fair English, that Leonard was known among the Navajos as Loose Ears. A moment later, Mrs. Huskon, a heavyset woman whose fingers were festooned with turquoise rings, and a daughter in her late teens, who was dressed in pink and purple silk and held a baby in her arms, came out of the hogan. The women stood apart from us and watched intently as Huskon handed Leonard a battered Carnation milk can containing some rock fragments. Leonard examined them and said, "Let's see the place."

The two Huskon men piled into the jeep with us, and, at Huskon's direction, we drove west for twenty minutes along a narrow road. Then, for an hour, Leonard skillfully coaxed his jeep up and down a series of dunes, until we came to a halt at the top of a slope that descended a hundred feet or so to the bank of a creek, where we all got out. The only discernible sign of life was a lizard that lay sprawled like a patch of pale-green sand a scant few inches from the jeep's right front wheel. Huskon nodded to Leonard and then plunged nimbly down the slope. Evans followed clumsily; Leonard, although encumbered by a Geiger counter he had taken out of the back of the car, could have easily passed him but diplomatically refrained from doing so. I brought up the rear. We walked along the creek a few yards and then Huskon stopped and pointed to some yellow-and-black sandstone partly hidden under a ledge. Leonard switched on his counter and, holding it close to the formation, studied the dial. "More," Huskon said, pointing ahead. We followed the outcrop for thirty yards and then stopped again. I could make out a yellowish glint under the ledge for at least another thirty yards. "The counter shows only a fair degree of radioactivity, but there seems to be so much of the rock that it's worth digging into to see what's back of the rim," Leonard said to me. "I'm going to suggest that the Commission do some drilling here." He turned to Huskon and said something in Navajo, concluding, in English, "I have hope. We will see." Huskon nodded earnestly.

"What do you think this rock can be used for?" I asked Huskon.

He studied Leonard's face briefly and then replied, "It is what the white man wants."

We returned to the jeep, and Leonard, after driving the Huskons back to their hogan, saw to it that I got to Grants and Paddy Martinez on schedule by letting me off in Flagstaff a few minutes before a mail train with seats for a dozen passengers pulled out. I rode it for three hundred and fifty miles and spent the night at the Motel Milan in Grants.

Grants, I came to realize the next day, was all Paddy Martinez. The Indian sheepherder's discovery on Haystack Mountain three years earlier had completely changed the town's way of life. Before he spotted his yellow ore, local boosters, by way of trumpeting what was then Grants' big money crop, called their community the Carrot Capital; now they want it known as the Uranium City. (Miniature sacks of uranium-ore chips, with mailing tags marked "Guaranteed Radioactive and Harmless" attached, are now on sale in shops there for a quarter apiece.) In the old days, Grants prided itself not on its carrots alone but on being the only place of any size along the hundred and thirty-five miles of Highway 66 that connect the cities of Albuquerque and Gallup — a distinction that brought it an assortment of motels and gas stations, with a reptile house by the name of Cobra Gardens in the midst of them. Approaching the town, one still sees such signs as "PEACE PIPES, 98c," "CACTUS HANKIES," and "DID YOU KNOW THERE ARE 55 KINDS OF RATTLESNAKES?"

These ancient glories are now dimmed by the big-time operations that have followed upon Paddy Martinez's strike. Millions of dollars are being spent on mine development and further exploration of the region. A considerable part of this money has been invested by the Sante Fe Railroad, which, under a government land grant authorized decades ago to encourage railroad building in the West, has turned out to be the legal owner of the mineral rights on the land where the uranium was found. The deposits of ore involved in Operation Haystack, as the Santa Fe has named its project, have proved extensive enough to justify the construction of a plant just outside Grants, which the Anaconda Copper Mining Company is building at a cost of three and a half million dollars. Anaconda has also signed a prospecting contract with the Laguna tribe of Indians, whose reservation is about eight miles from Grants, and is now putting up a housing development for its plant personnel. I learned most of this in the course of a talk I had with Carroll Gunderson, president of the Grants State Bank. Gunderson was mayor of Grants when, in the summer of 1950, Paddy — as Gunderson, and everybody else, calls him — brought him some samples of ore from Haystack Mountain, and after examining them he took them to a group of geologists from the Colorado School of Mines who happened to be in the vicinity conducting an experiment for the Defense Department. They were profoundly impressed.

Nearly everyone I talked to in Grants had a definite point of view about Paddy. A Commission geologist was pleased but deflated by what Paddy had found on Haystack — one of the largest uranium deposits so far discovered in the United States. Paddy, he said, not only had flown in the face of academic geology by finding uranium in a limestone formation but had done so in a most humiliating manner. "What a ludicrous location!" the geologist said. "Haystack — a mountain in full view of a transcontinental highway that thousands of tourists drive over all year long. Now Paddy's name is turning up in geology journals, and to some people, I guess, we look pretty silly." A good deal of the talk about Paddy had to do with what he was getting out of his strike, but no one I ran into appeared to have gone to the trouble of asking Paddy himself. It was understood that he had been put on the Santa Fe payroll, some thought for life (he was almost sixty at the time of his find), at a salary the size of which seemed to be anybody's guess. I talked to Grants residents who declared that Paddy was losing out to what they darkly termed "the interests"; several of these people also felt that when the Santa Fe moved in on him he became the victim of a thoroughly obsolete law. Other residents believed that Paddy was cleaning up, and predicted that he would squander his sudden wealth. One man said it was obvious that Paddy was doing all right. "He's the only Indian around these parts whose hogan has windows," he pointed out.

Stopping by at Paddy's hogan, I found that he hardly knows what to make of his lot. He and some of his family were shearing sheep when I arrived, and he led me through a flock of sheep and loudly bleating lambs to a large burlap sack filled with new fleece, on which we found comfortable seats. A husky, swarthy man with a single tooth, Paddy was wearing Navy fatigues and a sombrero. His voice was low, rasping, and lugubrious as he told me that the whole Haystack business started one day in April 1950 when he ran out of cigarettes. "I don't remember the date, but it was lambing season," he said. "I was on horseback, going along a trail to the Rattlesnake Trading Post for the cigarettes, when I saw this little yellow spot under some rock. I got off and dug it out with a stick, because it reminded me of the time in 1947 when I bought a bus ticket in Grants at the Yucca Hotel. Three white men were talking about an ore called uranium and saying it was worth a lot of money. They were showing some of it to each other and I got a look at it. It was the same yellow stuff I was holding in my hand on that trail. Well, I got my cigarettes and came home and told my wife I'd found some kind of ore. She didn't believe me. The next day, I went out with a pick and hammer and walked west along the edge of this rock for a mile and a half and kept finding more and more. I got on my horse and went east for five miles and found more.

"I got lots of friends — Americans, Indians, Mexicans. But I didn't trust anybody except maybe Ed Harmon — he's a farmer — and Mr. Gunderson. I had the whole thing on my mind for a week. Then I went to Ed and I said to him, 'Ed, I found an ore they call uranium. Help me fill out the blanks for the claims.' Ed filled out sixteen blanks for me in Grants. After that, I took some samples to Gunderson, and he told me that some college men from Colorado said they were good. I didn't know what to do. Then a fellow over on Mount Taylor heard about the ore and he wanted to dig. I didn't trust him, but he came around nine or ten times, so finally I said to him, 'O.K., but you stay right here and dig, and nothing else.' Well, the next thing I knew, he'd done plenty else — he'd put in a claim for where I already had one. I got mad, and he went and told everyone about the place. There must have been a thousand cars on Haystack Mountain in the next ten days. Then it came out that the Santa Fe owned all my claims, and now they mail me a check for two hundred and fifty dollars every month."

The income has brought Paddy complications of a middle-class sort, I gathered. "I'm in debt," he told me, waving vaguely toward his windowed hogan. "My wife bought a sewing machine and now she wants a washing machine. I have about fifteen children, and for the first time in years I'm seeing every one of them at meals, now they know there's going to be something to eat." Plainly, life had been simpler for Paddy before he set out for those cigarettes three years earlier. Back then, he said, he hadn't known where his next dollar was coming from, but a man who only raised a few sheep wasn't expected to know a thing like that. He had also earned a little money recruiting harvesters for the carrot growers and picking carrots himself. "You get dirty picking carrots, but it's clean dirt," he said. "You don't even need water for it. You can just wipe it off on your pants. Now, this uranium, they tell me it's used for a powder for some kind of bomb. Carrots you can eat. I'll take carrots. This damn uranium — my friends don't like me the same any more. Some of them are jealous of me and the others are mad at me because I didn't tell them about what I'd found. They think if I had, they might be getting checks the same as me. But carrots — there are no secrets about carrots. You're in an open field. If you stop picking for a minute and look around, there are the others picking. You can see them and they can see you. Everybody knows what everybody else is doing."

AN A-HOUSE WITH GARDEN

NEARLY ALL THE URANIUM that Paddy and his fellow prospectors find on the Colorado Plateau makes its way to Oak Ridge, the oldest and still the largest atomic-energy preserve in the country, where it is converted into nuclear ammunition. I had first seen Oak Ridge shortly after its existence was disclosed to the public, in 1945, when it was already three years old. Revisiting it, after the passage of nearly a decade, the town seemed to have retained much of its original jerry-built rawness, but in its appearance, if not in its activities, it was plainly developing into a small, sedate Southern city. The initial surprise, on seeing it again, is the paved sidewalks and roads, built under the auspices of the Atomic Energy Commission, which administers the sixty-thousand-acre area in the name of the federal government, which owns it. Back in the days when Oak Ridge was run by the Army, everybody was too preoccupied with other matters to fuss about urban refinements, and the town got along with narrow boardwalks and rutted dirt roads. There is still only one hotel in Oak Ridge, the Alexander, the flimsy two-story frame structure in which visiting physicists and military men were billeted during the frenzied days of the Manhattan District. A concrete wing has been added, a potted plant or two installed in the small lobby, and a brief, limp canopy set up over the entrance, but the major change is in the clientele. Friends and relatives of residents now stop at the Alexander, and so do traveling salesmen, whose line may be anything from machinery for the huge plants to lingerie; merchants who are thinking of leasing store space from the government; and scholars, some from foreign countries and many with eminent reputations, who come to take a month-long training course, given by the Oak Ridge Institute of Nuclear Studies, in the use of isotopes, the "tagged" atoms that are stimulating so much medical, agricultural, and industrial research.

Oak Ridge is far less crowded than it was in 1945. Its population then was seventy-five thousand; now it is thirty-one thousand. The great construction gangs of the secret years and the large military detail, which included a good many plainclothes counter-intelligence men, are gone. Simplified methods of separating U-235 from common uranium have reduced by thousands the staffs needed for the processing plants. Forty-five per cent of the twenty-three thousand employees live outside the area, in many cases to escape its institutionalized atmosphere and standardized housing. A hundred-acre stretch of ground where during the war twenty thousand construction men and their families were crammed into an unsightly trailer camp known as Happy Valley is now a meadow, with only a rusty hydrant here and there memorializing the congested colony. The landscape has also been decluttered by the removal of hundreds of creaky prefabricated houses, which the government sold at far below cost to neighboring optimists who believed they could put them to use. The result of all this is a tidier, more spacious community, and a temporary housing shortage.

Although permanent houses have been going up the last few years, the dominant architectural motif of Oak Ridge continues to be prefabrication. There are six categories of prefab, designated by letters of the alphabet and ranging from the A-house, which is small and has two bedrooms, to the height of prefabricated luxury — the F-house, with three bedrooms and a dining room. The residential section is also divided into categories. The bottom of the valley in which the town lies is the Low Amenity Zone; above it is the Medium Amenity Zone; and above that the High Amenity Zone, which provides considerable privacy and a sweeping view of the Cumberland Mountains. The monotony of the houses depresses many residents, but most are consoled by the rents. "Can you imagine how crazy I'd sound back in Chicago if I asked a real-estate man for a six-room house with a lawn for $45.46," a young housewife said to me. "My rent check is the first one I mail out each month — and always with thanksgiving. Besides, this town is full of bright high-school kids. Thirty-five cents an hour for a baby-sitter! In Chicago, sitters got a dollar an hour, and I had to buy a television set." The best houses in Oak Ridge rent for around seventy-five dollars a month, a sum that anyone in Oak Ridge, where there is no unemployment and where the average wage, not counting in baby-sitters, is about eighty-five dollars a week, could probably afford. In assigning homes, the Housing Division takes into account the size of family, but the choicest generally go to the top scientists and administrators. "We have a two-billion-dollar investment here," an official told me, "and we can't forget for a minute that our most important asset is the people with the brains to run it."

Although Oak Ridge is as purposeful as ever, producing nuclear explosive around the clock, its residents appear a good deal more relaxed than they did when I was there last. Everyone I talked to then was itching to get his job over with and go back where he had come from. Most of the present inhabitants seem to be planning to stick around. A survey conducted by the University of

Tennessee in 1951, at the request of the Oak Ridge Chamber of Commerce, showed that eighty per cent of the residents had come to regard Oak Ridge as their permanent home. "Just a few years ago," I was told by Tom Clines, a department-store manager, "you'd ask a child what his home town was and he'd say 'Greensboro, North Carolina,' or wherever. Nowadays, he'd say 'Oak Ridge.'" Mrs. Elizabeth Anderson, a member of the medical-research staff, told me that the change of attitude became noticeable when the paving began, in September, 1946. "The following spring, there was a spontaneous wave of serious gardening," she said. "By the summer of 1948, when they got around to the side streets, we were boring each other with news about our gardens. By 1949, we had sidewalks, and the community had, I think, sunk its own roots as well as the roots of its flowers."

Since 1950, three new schools and nineteen churches have been built, and these, of course, have added to the town's air of permanence. So has the arrival of insurance firms, a brokerage house, a travel bureau, and an assortment of other white-collar enterprises that do not usually infiltrate bivouac areas. Perhaps the crowning proof of Oak Ridge's stability was the appearance, in the spring of 1953, of a loan company — the Atomic Indorsement Loan Company. As it happens, this is the first firm there to use the magic word in its name. "Very corny," a gas-station attendant told me. "I'm sure the owner has found out by now that down here 'atomic' isn't a word to fool around with. It's business to us." For pleasure, Oak Ridge has a full-size amateur symphony orchestra, which grew out of a smaller wartime outfit called the Symphonette and which has had such guest recitalists as Isaac Stern and Percy Grainger. Late in 1952, it presented the world première of "Overture to the Dedication of a Nuclear Reactor," composed by Dr. Arthur Roberts, a physicist at the University of Rochester. There is also a little-theater group, an art circle, a few movie houses, including one that occasionally shows a foreign film, and a newspaper, the *Oak Ridger*. A country club, whose members built the clubhouse and laid out an eighteen-hole golf course, has been in operation since 1947. "We're not wealthy and we're in a dry county, so the club is more golf than country," a charter member told me. "Just about anyone who is willing to pony up can join. I doubt if it'll get snobbish as long as scientists are our local aristocrats."

About a hundred and fifty other organizations, ranging from fraternal lodges to the Coon Hunters Association, the African Violet Club, the Great Books Club, and the Mental Hygiene Workshop, are flourishing in the town, to the displeasure of some of the old settlers, who remember when Oak Ridgers had little use for such extracurricular diversions. "In the early days, a few homesick fellows might form an Alabama Club or something like that, but most of us were too excited to care about that sort of thing," a biochemist who has been here since 1943 told me. "The wartime ferment seems to have just about died out, but, judging from the number of people who left and then came back, I guess Oak Ridge hasn't lost all its zest." Another ten-year veteran, Thomas F. X. McCarthy, a technical-reports analyst who was born and raised in New York, assured me that he has had no regrets about settling down in Oak Ridge. "I'm a happy expatriate," he remarked. "I'm not going to call New York a nice place to visit, but I will say that Tennessee is a nice place to live in. Things aren't frantic here. You're not dizzied by neon lights and gas fumes, and, thanks to the fashion standards of the scientists, you don't have to wear a tie or a hat. Sure, I miss all the plays and night clubs in New York, but, come to think of it, when the hell did I ever go to them?"

In March 1949, when the Atomic Energy Commission got around to revising the wartime security system, Oak Ridge was declared an open city. Residents no longer had to show identification badges to get in or out. Visitors no longer required passes. Previously, the entire area had been enclosed by a fence, with carefully guarded gates; now part of the fence came down, and only the controlled, or plant, area remained enclosed and under special guard. A cavalcade of celebrities, including Senator Kefauver, Marie McDonald, Adolphe Menjou, and Vice-President Barkley, came down to hail the end of wartime security as a boon to the citizens of Oak Ridge and a possible omen of lasting world peace. They might have made a little less of the occasion if they had known the state of mind of many of their listeners, who dreaded losing the protection from the outside world that the security regulations, which had been designed to conceal even the identity of Oak Ridge's chief enterprise, had given them. Their xenophobia reached so high a pitch that, for six months before the gates were opened, the administrative authorities conducted a campaign of public meetings, press statements, and personal talks in an effort to calm everybody down. At one of the meetings, I was told, a scientist's wife burst into tears and said she would no longer dare let her daughters walk to school. People complained that at night they would have to lock their doors and remove the keys from their cars. (There are few private garages in Oak Ridge.) Others feared a swarm of peddlers. A chemist from unfenced Boston bought two 12-gauge shotguns to defend his home against marauders. "It was odd," Gordon R. Molesworth, Assistant to the Manager of Oak Ridge Operations, told me, "but as soon as the gates were open, the whole outcry died."

In the summer of 1953, in a spirit of economy and confidence, the Commission discharged a hundred and forty guards and opened the three main roads through the plant area to the public. Now the plants are protected only by their individual fences and guards. Since K-25, a gaseous diffusion plant, and Y-12, an electromagnetic separation plant, are within sight of the newly opened roads, many drivers going through Oak Ridge on their way somewhere else stop to stare at the esoteric factories that, for better or worse, are shaping their futures.

The only organized tourist attraction is the American Museum of Atomic Energy, which exhibits such objects as specimens of uranium ore, Geiger counters, and models of separation plants. It has been visited by more than eighteen thousand people in some summer months. Guides are on hand to show sightseers around and rattle off the history of atomic energy. I discovered on one of these tours that the Museum is not above a touch or two of nuclear frivolity. There is a slot machine — a lead-shielded receptacle containing antimony beryllium, a source of neutrons — in which you insert a dime and get it back in a plastic case marked "American Museum of Atomic Energy, Neutron Irradiated." Farther along, the guide calls for a volunteer "without a wig" to put his hands on a particle accelerator that generates two hundred and fifty thousand volts at an extremely low amperage, the effect of which is to make his hair stand on end. The tour ends with a demonstration of the flexibility of the mechanical hands used in the manipulation of radioactive materials; the guide, operating the steel fingers by remote control, lights someone's cigarette, and, as a final flourish, applies lipstick at approximately the right place on a lady tourist. "We may not have made you experts, but we trust that you are leaving the museum junior atomic scientists at least," the guide declared when it was all over.

While the great majority of its residents look upon Oak Ridge as their home town, none of them owns a home there, or, for that matter, a square foot of land. A survey made by the Census Bureau in 1952 indicated that sixty per cent of them would be interested in buying houses if the government ever decides to put them up for sale. Among most tenants, the urge to build a basement or a garage is chilled by the knowledge that it would become the property of the government. While the government does see to it that all the houses are painted periodically, its decorative efforts are accepted joylessly. "Eight standard colors, and like as not you pick the same one as your best friend," a housewife complained to me. "It's as though everyone went to a party in identical dresses." There aren't enough shops, and there probably won't be until businessmen are permitted to build on land that belongs to them. A haberdasher I talked with, who has a fifteen-year lease on his store, said, "People here are so government-conscious they don't even realize a fellow can be in business for himself. If they get sore about a shirt or hat they've bought in my place, they don't threaten to take their trade elsewhere. They tell me they're going to report me to the Atomic Energy Commission."

To offset such socialistic irritations, Oak Ridge has a number of advantages over communities that are not owned and subsidized by the government. There are no city taxes. The Commission foots the bill for garbage collection, the police force, the fire department, and the schools. Rents run a third or so lower than they do for comparable houses in the surrounding area. Many people are worried about losing all this if the government decides to go out of business as a landlord.

As for the Atomic Energy Commission, it couldn't be more eager to get rid of this uneconomical headache. Several syndicates have offered to buy the residential and shopping sections lock, stock, and barrel, but the Commission has turned them down on the ground that monopoly ownership would lead to a speculators' field day. It has, however, evolved a plan for disposing of as much property as possible to as many people as possible in an orderly fashion. "It's a highly complex affair," Molesworth told me. "No city this size has ever been sold. But we think we've got a good system of priorities to determine who gets first crack at what. We're confident that the Oak Ridge brand of Socialism will sooner or later start creeping backward."

One of the people who are rooting hardest for private ownership is Fred W. Ford, the Director of Community Affairs, whose job is pretty much that of mayor. He is a soft-spoken, harried Bostonian whose New England conscience has long been tortured by the low rent he pays for his F-house, High Amenity Zone. "Ever since I came here, in 1948, my job has been to work myself out of a job and let the people run things for themselves," he told me.

Although Oak Ridge is the fifth largest city in Tennessee, it has still not been incorporated, which means that the residents have considerably less voice in their own local government than the Atomic Energy Commission or the State of Tennessee has. Many of the matters that other towns settle for themselves are decided for Oak Ridge — some in Washington and others in Nashville. Legislatively, the issue of incorporation, which is a problem for the State, has no connection with the issue of private ownership, but in the minds of some Oak Ridgers the two tend to get entangled. Practically everyone I talked to would like to see Oak Ridge incorporated someday, but when the prevailing sentiment was tested by a referendum in March 1953 the vote went four to one against immediate incorporation. "Don't buy a pig in a poke," a labor leader had cautioned the townspeople, and apparently this gifted phrase reflects a widespread reluctance to ditch the benevolent autocracy of Uncle Sam.

Whatever its eventual status is to be, Oak Ridge is continuing to develop rapidly. Its plant and research facilities are constantly being expanded. K-25, already valued at six hundred and fifty million dollars, is being enlarged by a new unit whose cost will come to four hundred and sixty-four million. On a smaller scale, its private businesses are coming in for their share of expansion. "Our object is to catch more and more of those tourists," the head of the Chamber of Commerce told me. "We're going to put up highway signs and flood bus stations with folders. We want to attract more business here. We want to make Oak Ridge a normal town." But, however far Oak Ridge progresses in this direction, it will probably never quite become a normal town as long as K-25, sprawling in its small river valley below wooded ridges, continues to burn its thousands of lights through the night. To an outsider, it would seem that only history, which was the town's progenitor, has the power to fulfill Oak Ridge's aspiration of becoming an ordinary place.

viii

CAMELLIAS AND BOMBS

EIGHT YEARS AFTER THE FOUNDING of Oak Ridge, construction of its hydrogen-bomb counterpart, the first plant designed to further the production of that momentous weapon, was started on a three-hundred-square-mile tract of land surrounding the town of Ellenton in south central South Carolina. When I visited this once agricultural area, which borders the Savannah River, hundreds of graders, tractors, and bulldozers were noisily converting it to its new purpose. A four-lane highway, extending nineteen miles to North Augusta, South Carolina, had been built to accommodate first, the heavy traffic of the building phase and, later, that accompanying the operation of the factory and its laboratories. A large administration building, newly erected on what was part of a peanut farm, was being used as a headquarters by Atomic Energy Commission officials and the managerial and engineering representatives of the Explosives and Engineering Departments of the du Pont Company, which, as the government's dollar-for-the-whole-job contractor, was overseeing the construction of the plant, the cost of which was estimated at nine hundred million dollars. (It has since risen to one and a half billion dollars.) One-eighth of the seven thousand people who were living in the area when the government decided to condemn it (the local press called them "the D.P.s of W.W. III") had already made way for the weapon, moving, most of them, just beyond the perimeter of the budding reservation. Thanks to the appearance of four house movers, many of these D.P.s were still living in their homes, which for the most part are sharecropper shacks and modest farmhouses. The first of the house movers, a man by the name of Ralph South, set out for South Carolina from Ordway, Colorado, on November 28, 1950, the day the government announced the project. The house movers were also towing churches to new locations, and, under the supervision of Army engineers, about a hundred cemeteries were to be shifted, at government expense.

The remainder of the seven thousand residents were gradually being eased out by the expanding construction. The site was soon to be overrun by the work crews, and the entire pre-November 28th population, many of whose forebears settled there before the Revolution, established elsewhere. The tardier of the dispossessed were witnessing changes that they found only slightly less startling than they had found the announcement that they would have to leave. "A stranger used to mean a revenue agent after moonshiners," a tenant farmer remarked to me. "But this, it's made *us* the strangers." On Sundays, an average of a thousand visitors, out on rubberneck jaunts, had been driving into Ellenton (pop. 700), the largest town on the site, and piling out of their cars to inquire eagerly of the first native they came across, "Where are they making that bomb?" On weekdays, the lingering residents could count on seeing five thousand other outlanders, the complement of the construction force. Every day brought a new batch of migratory construction workers lumbering through Ellenton in trailers that bore the license plates of distant states. Many of them hoped to find jobs, having heard that, at its peak, the construction roster was to reach 35,000; by that time the farming community having vanished, newcomers would be newcomers only to project workers of senior standing. When these thousands of people were through with their job, the tall smokestacks of our most modern oven, the nuclear reactor, would tower above the vestiges of pastures and cotton plantations.

The plant that was being built by the Savannah River Operations Office, to use the project's singularly unspecific official name, was to be related to the hydrogen bomb in much the same way that the plants at Oak Ridge are related to the atomic bomb; that is, the weapon itself would not be assembled there but in some other part of the country. Only fuels required by a hydrogen bomb were to be made there. One is plutonium, which, if international tensions ever permit, can also be employed to create power for peacetime needs. Another, which has yet to be officially identified, is good for destruction and nothing else. Aside from these facts, the authorities of the Savannah River Operations Office would disclose nothing of a technical nature about their work, but even this scant information was enough, at the time it was revealed, to engender a widespread fear in near-by Aiken and Augusta, Georgia, as well as in smaller communities, that the construction of the plan might result in the Soviet Union's deciding to drop an atomic bomb on one of our hydrogen bombs. This particular worry, according to one official of the Atomic Energy Commission, had been pretty well allayed by government speakers, who, in scores of addresses to local civic groups and fraternal orders, harped on the point that the bomb would not be put together in or near Ellenton. "Of course," the same official said to me, "the bomb will have to be assembled *somewhere,* but we'll let somebody else worry about that." The orators also gave assurances that the plant's radioactive fuels would not harm people living in the vicinity. "Now, about those fish in the Savannah River," George O. Robinson, the project's information officer, said at a Rotary meeting in Augusta. "A man catching them from the banks of the Savannah at its nearest point to the plant would have to eat eight pounds of them every day for the rest of his life before he would approach the radiation tolerance we'll allow our employees inside the factory." Mrs. Mattie Hall, an antique dealer in Aiken, told me that the mere arrival of the construction workers from other parts of the country had had as reassuring an effect on the population as all the government's carefully worded statements. "At first, everybody wanted to run away," she said. "Then we saw these fellows pouring in from every state and we changed our minds. We decided that living here couldn't really be so dangerous if all these men were coming in with their families. Maybe they won't stay on when the plant is built and starts to operate, but it doesn't seem likely they'd have brought their families with them unless they planned to stay. By now, we've convinced ourselves that the plant's going to be protected all day long by Air Force planes and that we'll all be just terribly safe."

Most of the people with homes near the site were uncertain about how the project would affect their way of life. A number of the businessmen, however, were definitely enthusiastic, for the plant was to be one of the largest industrial developments in the Southeast. "It's as if a hundred new industries were settling down in our fair city," Lester C. Moody, the secretary of the Augusta Chamber of Commerce, told me. "It's going to mean empire-building to us. Augusta is going to grow and grow and be prosperous. Of course, the folks around Ellenton are being inconvenienced, but you can't have progress with sentiment." Then he added majestically, "The hand that shuns the thorn can't have the rose."

The government, needless to say, was not primarily concerned with local inconvenience or prosperity in choosing its site. A committee spent four months examining likely sites in twenty-five states and, in all, considered over a hundred locations. "We almost located near Terre Haute and Paris, Texas," Curtis A. Nelson, the Atomic Energy Commission's project manager, told me, "but neither of these places could quite match the combination of factors here in South Carolina." Perhaps the most important factor was one that Nelson guardedly referred to as "technical considerations." "If I described them, I might be giving away the process we're planning to use," he said to me. The proximity to sources of power — the Savannah River and the Clark Hill hydroelectric dam — was another inducement, Nelson said. Interstate highways were at hand. So were two rail lines. Engineers studied the soil and found it suitable for the support of heavy buildings. There were no natural obstacles, such as mountains or dense forests, to slow up construction work. The closest atomic-energy installation was three hundred miles away, at Oak Ridge, and this fact appealed to the advocates of dispersal. The land, much of it uncultivated, was comparatively cheap and thinly populated. Only a small percentage of the two hundred thousand acres would actually be occupied by the plant and its laboratories, Nelson said, but it would be necessary to have a good deal of land around them to avoid what he called "possible hazards" to the surrounding countryside and to prevent unauthorized persons from getting near the installation. "There'll be plenty of space left over for the quail, deer, and wild turkeys," Nelson said. "They're not being asked to evacuate. It may even be possible to permit the South Carolina Wild Life Federation to plant food crops for them in a swampy section along the Savannah. If that works out, they'll probably be living in the world's best-guarded sanctuary."

In the course of a talk I had with Arthur Tackman, Nelson's assistant, I learned that a survey made by the Federal Housing Administration also had quite a lot to do with selecting the site. The survey had been undertaken to ascertain how well the towns near the area — primarily Augusta and Aiken — could absorb the influx of workers. The F.H.A. turned in an optimistic report on the availability of housing in these communities, on their schools and hospitals, and on the ability of local banks to lend money for building additional facilities. "Many people have asked why the plant isn't being built in an even more sparsely populated place," Tackman said. "I understand that President Truman himself asked that when he was shown our plans. But the Atomic Energy Commission has been putting a new policy into effect, and this made us locate within a few miles of fair-sized communities. Right here we've got one of the least populated spots in the United States that's near such communities and that meets our other requirements." The policy, Tackman explained, was not to set up any more government towns, like the ones at Oak Ridge, Los Alamos, and Hanford.

"They had to be built because everything was so secret during the war, but in general the government hates government towns," Tackman said. A government town, he went on, has to start from scratch, and entails the great expense of houses, churches, schools, streets, and police and fire forces, and there are so many headaches connected with running a town of that sort that the officials in charge are apt to be distracted from their main job of turning out weapons. "You paint somebody's house first and everybody else starts squawking," Tackman said. "Some people want Venetian blinds, others won't stand for them. And everybody has the same landlord — the government itself — and the government gets kicked around enough even when it's not a landlord. Also, we don't think it's a good idea for people who work together to have to live together. You might work all day alongside someone you didn't like and then have him as a neighbor at night. And a man who loses his job in a government town loses much more than that. He has to get off the reservation in thirty days, and that means he loses his home, his wife loses her social circle, his children lose their schools. Besides, Americans don't really like to live in government towns. It makes them feel as though they were being deprived of some of their independence. It's an intangible thing.

I don't believe Americans are even keen about living in enormous privately owned housing projects."

Augusta (pop. 71,000), one of the two towns on which the success of the government's anti-government policy was most dependent, was expected to play its part without undue difficulty. About Aiken (pop. 7,000), the other town, a lovely community and one of the horsiest winter resorts in America, there was, however, considerable speculation as to whether it would be "spoiled." Some of the wealthiest and oldest families in the United States were in the habit of spending the winters in their fine homes along Whiskey Road, the highway that, after passing through their neighborhood, continues, as Route 19, on to the government's development, fourteen miles away. Most of the town's broad avenues, bisected by island parks planted with pin oaks and magnolias, were still unpaved, out of consideration for the sensitivity of horses' hoofs. The Hitchcock Woods, an eleven-thousand-acre park where no automobiles were permitted, provided a highly attractive setting for riders. The horses of some of the nation's leading racing stables, the majority of which are owned by Northerners, wintered there. Many Derby winners have had their débuts at the annual Aiken Trials, on the beautifully laid-out Mile Track. Hunts helped to pass away the short winter days. Aiken was one of America's polo centers. For those of the winter residents who were not entirely engrossed with riding, one of the country's seven court-tennis courts was available at the Aiken Tennis Club, and for golfers there was the Palmetto Golf Club's superb course. "We know Aiken as a simple country town," S. A. Warner Baltazzi, a retired bank president, told me when I called on him at his Whiskey Road home.

Whether Aiken was to retain its simplicity hinged on the manner of its impending growth. Many townspeople feared that their community would lose its appeal as a resort town if it were invaded by large numbers of construction workers and plant employees. This would seriously upset Aiken's economy, which had long been firmly based on the winter colony. At the same time, the townspeople hoped to see their incomes increased by the spending of the new arrivals. "We shouldn't have to make a choice between the winter colony and the people the plant will bring here," one fairly agitated shopkeeper told me. "That can be avoided if the right people are attracted — scientists, engineers, government officials. The winter residents have their houses and stables here, and I know they want to stay, but will they if these construction workers trespass on their estates? They've got the money to lead a secluded life with, and if they can't find it here, they'll probably look for it elsewhere." Another Aikenite with whom I talked, Albert Howell, an editor of the Aiken *Standard & Review,* was less perturbed about the likelihood of the town's being swamped by construction workers. "They'll go to Augusta," he predicted confidently. "This town's too dull for them. No night clubs, no roadhouses. You can get liquor in South Carolina only between sunrise and sunset, and you have to buy it by the bottle and drink it in somebody's home. No bars. Their big Saturday night would be dismal. All they could do would be sit in a restaurant and drink beer until midnight, when the blue laws take over. But Augusta is wide open."

The winter residents with whom I talked seemed far less exercised about the construction workers than were the native Aikenites. (None of them talked of "riffraff," as several of the townspeople did.) Their principal concern was to preserve their agreeable privacy. Some intrusions, to be sure, had already occurred, but these were taken more or less in stride. For example, Gracefields, a seven-thousand-acre hunting preserve near Ellenton that was formerly leased by Mrs. W. R. Grace, of the shipping family, for shooting parties, had been acquired by the government as part of its site. "Oh, well, there's no point crying," Mrs. Grace assured me philosophically. "I've had a good time. The hydrogen bomb hasn't been the only surprise. This past winter, we had one of our coldest snaps and the camellias went. And, of course, in New York the Ritz-Carlton's come down. I lived there for eight years." One of the few kind words I heard for construction workers came from Terence Preece, one of the country's best polo players, who had been making his living by training ponies and promoting matches in Aiken and elsewhere. "Those I've seen so far are rabid polo fans," he said. "We've sold more dollar admissions this year than ever before."

The traffic on Whiskey Road had increased to the point where some horsemen, trying to cross it in order to enter the Hitchcock Woods, were annoyed by the delays and danger to them and their mounts. Those dowagers who liked to shop were inclined to wish the stores were less crowded. "So many new faces," one of them said to me. "It's bewildering." Ten trailer camps had been set up between Aiken and the site of the plant, with more to come, and although the fashionable district of the town was protected by zoning laws, the camps were not very far away and some of the old-timers found the informality of their new neighbors' homes disconcerting.

The feeling along Whiskey Road was that the hibernating grounds of the winter people would be left alone. "What would a construction worker want with court tennis or drag hunts?" asked one Northerner with whom I discussed the subject. "Maybe he's done some skeet shooting, but we go in for live pigeons at the Gun Club. Why, a day there would set the fellow back thirty dollars. A dollar a pigeon, you know, plus a ten-dollar sweepstakes, cartridges, and the rest. Let's suppose that someone from the trailer crowd was put up for the Palmetto. He'd have to fork out two hundred and forty dollars for a membership fee, and five dollars for greens fees whenever he played. Or take it all from a New York angle: Does anyone at the Racquet Club care what happens on the West Side? You talk to people around here and they'll tell you that inheritance taxes are a hell of a lot worse nuisance than this hydrogen bomb." Mrs. C. Oliver Iselin, a handsome elderly lady who had been spending her winters in Aiken since she was a child, told me that she was rather looking forward to the arrival in Aiken of certain project employees. (She was in exuberant spirits, her trainer having just phoned her from the Jamaica track that one of her horses had won a race.) "I think the heads of departments would make interesting additions," she said. "There's a beautiful forty-four-acre section of my property on which I'm ready to let twenty-five of them build houses, provided the character of the property is preserved."

The winter resident who had undoubtedly made the happiest adjustment to the presence of the construction workers was Mr. Fitch Gilbert, an extremely affable Whiskey Road man of sixty-eight who owned a large tract of farmland adjoining the government site. Mr. Gilbert had opened a trailer camp on his property that would accommodate four hundred families. "My family is horsy, but I'm not," he told me. "I've tried a lot of things on that farm, winters, to keep busy — corn, wood, peanuts, cheese, cotton, cattle, and whatnot — but this trailer camp is the best thing yet. Four hundred families at eight dollars a week — why, that'll be more money than I've made in a long time. Some of my competitors are charging six dollars, but I'm not making my customers pay for electricity and I'm letting them have unlimited hot water. A plumber was telling me the other day that the one thing women want in a trailer camp is hot water. I may even throw in a few washing machines. I've named my camp Pine-Shade, to get over the idea that it doesn't sit out in the broiling sun, the way the others do. It's in a grove three hundred yards back from the road and only a mile from an artificial lake. My farmer put me on to the idea. I'm letting him run the camp's food store. He's been wanting to get ahead for a long time. Well, now he's getting ahead." Mr.

Gilbert was absolutely certain there would be no exodus from Whiskey Road. "Hell, no!" he said. "We'll stay until we pass on."

While Aiken was waiting uneasily to see what the project would do to it, the project's effect on Ellenton and the requisitioned land around it was one of utter finality. The residents, quite naturally, were stunned by the fate that had been visited on them by the government. They couldn't understand why their community had to be the one spot in the United States to attract the Atomic Energy Commission for its new project. "This is the worst thing that's happened since Sherman marched through," a South Carolina congressman declared in an interview in the local press. A Negro sharecropper indignantly asked his employer, "Why doesn't the Klan do something about this?" It is not unusual in Bible Belt country to find wooden signs with crudely lettered religious exhortations posted along the highway. After the government's announcement, signs of a secular nature went up, such as:

IT IS HARD TO UNDERSTAND WHY OUR TOWN MUST BE DESTROYED TO MAKE A BOMB THAT WILL DESTROY SOMEONE ELSE'S TOWN THAT THEY LOVE AS MUCH AS WE LOVE OURS. BUT WE FEEL THAT THEY PICKED NOT JUST THE BEST SPOT IN THE U.S. BUT IN THE WORLD.

WE LOVE THESE DEAR HEARTS AND GENTLE PEOPLE WHO LIVE IN OUR HOME TOWN.

WE'RE LIKE THE BOLL WEEVIL — LOOKING FOR A HOME.

The Ellentonians' shock was all the greater because it was unexpected. For several weeks before the announcement, they had watched engineers set up drill rigs at various points to plumb the soil. They had no idea what was going on, and invented a variety of rumors: The engineers had been assigned to find a site for a glue factory, a cotton-goods factory, an aluminum plant; they were prospecting for oil, uranium, kaolin. Each of these rumors was

greeted as good news, for while there was still some profitable
bale-to-the-acre land near Ellenton, cotton, once the region's
money crop, had long been on the decline, because of the boll
weevil's destructiveness and the increasing shortage of farm labor.
"We wanted an industry, but instead we all got drafted — men,
women, and children," Judge P. H. Buckingham, the town's magis-
trate, told me. The government came forward with assurances to
soften the blow: Department of Agriculture agents would assist
farmers in finding fertile new acreage; Ellenton residents would
be given first consideration for project jobs; assessors of their properties would take inflationary real-estate prices into account. Despite all such palliatives, a wild hope persisted that the edict would
somehow be rescinded. The hope withered in December 1950,
when Mr. Nelson and several of his colleagues appeared at a meeting in Ellenton to answer any questions that might be troubling
the townspeople. A member of the audience asked whether Ellentonians would be given the opportunity to buy back their land if
by some chance the project should ever be shut down. "We came
here not just to build a war plant but to make things that can be
used for peace," Mr. Nelson replied. "We plan to be with you a
long time."

At the time of my visit, there was an almost lively, if muted,
air of enterprise in and around Ellenton. The still-undisplaced
residents, using whatever ingenuity they were endowed with, were
contriving to make the best of their common accident. Merchants
were looking over near-by towns for likely places to do business.
Farmers were busy scouting for acreage; some had searched as
far as two hundred miles away, but the majority were trying to
stay close to Ellenton. A number of the older farmers had decided
to retire, and most of their tenants and sharechoppers had applied
for positions with the project. "If I get that job, it'll pay me more
than I've ever made," one tenant farmer told me. "I want to be
the chauffeur for a government official. I know a good fishing

hole to take him to." Mike Cassels, the owner of the general store and the rich man of Ellenton, was spending many hours poring over plans for his new home, to be built on Whiskey Road, not far from Mrs. Iselin's place. "I can't figure the architect out," he said to me. "I told him I wanted a comfortable home, not an expensive one. The last time he was in to see me, I said to him, 'Make a couple of mistakes in those damned plans if you want, but get the price down.' " Probably the most time-consuming activity was the endless deliberating over the best price that could realistically be expected of the government agents when they got around to assessing a property. "In the last month or so," I was told by Hunter Kennedy, one of Mr. Nelson's assistants, "they've been hounding us to hurry up and make them an offer for their land. They're impatient to find out what the future has in store for them."

Anticipation of the assessor's visit, helpful as it was, had not entirely distracted the Ellentonians from their plight. There were too many cheerless reminders of the community's imminent disappearance for that — fields reverting to brush, houses in disrepair, empty shelves in the stores. The thing that most bothered the citizens was the uprooting of the aged. No one I talked to in Ellenton failed to mention this. "Nobody's worried about the old folks who are well off, but about how the sick and poor ones can possibly get along someplace else," said Dr. Fred C. Brinkley, who had been the town's physician and druggist since 1910. "Still, some of these old sharecroppers have been here right along for years and years, and I never heard anyone worrying much about them until now, when the town's breaking up. I think it's just that people are taking stock of the kind of place they made it while it was alive. Whenever anything dies, people wonder if they couldn't have treated it nicer."

A FAREWELL TO
STRING AND SEALING WAX

DR. SAMUEL A. GOUDSMIT, a reflective and genial, though occasionally sardonic, man in his early fifties who is one of the nation's leading physicists, readily agrees with the popular view that recent developments in the field of atomic energy may profoundly affect future generations, if any, but he is more specifically concerned with the immediate effect the current scientific boom is having on him and his colleagues. The boom, in fact, has Dr. Goudsmit reeling. Sometimes, when his sardonic mood is on him, he wonders whether the synchrotons, the betatrons, the cosmotrons, and all the other contrivances physicists have lately rigged up to create energy by accelerating particles of matter aren't playing a wry joke on their inventors. "They're accelerating us, too," he says, in a voice that still betrays a trace of the accent of his native Holland. In protesting against the speedup, Goudsmit can speak with authority, for in the course of only a few years, he, like many other contemporary physicists, has seen his way of life change from a tranquil one of contemplation to a rat race. In 1941, as a professor of physics, he was contentedly dividing his time between laboratory and classroom at the University of Michigan; now, after having twice served overseas with the armed forces, he is the senior scientist and the chairman of the Physics Department at the Brookhaven National Laboratory, at Upton, Long Island, one of the largest nuclear-research centers in the United States, as well as the editor of the *Physical Review,* a professional journal that is to physicists all over the world what *Variety* is to show people and *Scott's Catalogue* to philatelists. Every now and then, when he encounters a stranger at a cocktail party or in the club car of a New York-to-Washington train, Goudsmit finds himself listening to a heated denunciation of physicists and all their works. "If it weren't for those damn scientists and their bombs, everything would be all right," says the stranger. Goudsmit turns his soft, brown, unhappy eyes toward the stranger and nods sympathetically, but it is an effort for him to restrain himself from setting the record straight. *"He* tells *me* that the scientists are upsetting everybody," he said recently after one such attack. "They've made him move his family to the country, he says, and he hates commuting. And what do I do? Do I tell him that it's the lives of us physicists that have really been upset? Do I tell him that the hot and cold wars have so changed my profession that I can hardly recognize it any more? I do not. I just say that country air is good for kids, and try to change the subject. What spineless self-restraint! Why don't I have the courage to tell him that we physicists are among the maladjusted veterans of the Second World War?"

Before the war, to hear Goudsmit tell it, physicists were a poor but happy lot. There were relatively few of them, and they kept pretty much to themselves. Those were what he calls "the string-and-sealing-wax days" — an allusion to the makeshift materials with which physicists often put their rudimentary apparatus together in cramped laboratories somewhere out behind the gym on this or that university campus. Nowadays, both government and industry are pumping billions of dollars into this once impoverished profession. "It's been a shock," Goudsmit says. "We've got marvelous laboratories for basic research, which is the real love of any self-respecting physicist, but somehow we don't have the same tender affection for them that we would have had years ago, when acquiring a three-hundred-dollar spectroscope was reason enough for throwing a party. Today we're given a multi-million-dollar piece of equipment, and the minute the dedication ceremonies are over, we're poring over plans for an even more powerful one. In the old days physicists gave themselves up wholly to a single-minded study of the fundamental laws of the universe. Now we feel called upon to do things of a sort we never even imagined we'd be doing — thoroughly unscientific things. We sit down with the Defense Secretary to help him figure out his next year's budget. We brief the President of the United States on the nation's nuclear stockpile. We're at Eniwetok or Las Vegas, or we're talking with troop commanders in Europe or Japan. We teach physics to Navy officers who are going to run nuclear-powered submarines. Air Force generals used to be just newsreel figures to us, but now they're fellows we have to talk over atomic-driven planes and plan offensive and defensive tactics with. Some of us are in industry, designing electronic equipment, and some of us are attached to the American embassy staffs in England, France, and Germany. Colleagues of mine who never even bothered to vote before Hiroshima now sit at the elbows of our United Nations representatives when the subject of atomic energy is on the agenda. And others, who were ill at ease lecturing before a few seminar students, now address large audiences on the fate that threatens the world if atomic energy is not internationally controlled. From timid pedagogue to eloquent Jeremiah — all in the space of a few short years."

Goudsmit himself has done a stint or two as a Jeremiah. On one occasion, in 1949, he delivered a stirring message on the subject of atomic weapons from the rostrum of a Tex and Jinx television show. "It was quite a production," he recalls, with a grimace of stricken incredulity. "Boy Scouts were on the program. So was the pilot who dropped the bomb on Hiroshima. He said that war was hell. I was introduced to Johnny, the Philip Morris midget. A United Nations chorus of twenty-five voices sang 'Rock of Ages,' and there were two ducks, one of them radioactive, in the cast. My daughter Esther, who was sixteen then, was in the studio, and when I came off the stage, she gave me a big hug and told me I was terrific. She wanted me to take a screen test right away."

Sometimes, when Goudsmit sits back and surveys the scene of contemporary physics, he becomes exasperated by the imperturbable calm with which many of the younger scientists around him — men who have never known the rigors of the string-and-sealing-wax days — address themselves to the momentous, and to him shattering, new order of things. This group of self-assured newcomers is quite large, for half of those who hold Ph.D.s in physics at the present time are under twenty-five. "All these young fellows grew up with the war and some of them were in it," Goudsmit says. "By and large they seem to have been less disturbed by it than the older men. They give you the impression they're just trying to get ahead. Of course, I realize it's not their fault that they weren't around in the old days, but I can't help wishing they'd stop acting as though the profession had always been the way it is now — if only out of respect for old men like me. Lord, the expensive equipment they expect! I gulp at some of the vouchers I'm called on to sign out at Brookhaven. Right now, it seems, everybody there wants a new type of oscilloscope that sells for thirty-five hundred dollars. Someone walked into my office the other day and complained that he had to share the one we'd got for him with another researcher. These new machines do make the work easier, but that doesn't keep me from wondering if, in the long run, it's best for everyone to own a Cadillac. Oh, well, I'm probably in my dotage."

Currently, Goudsmit points out, a young man of average ability who has a desire to earn a Ph.D. in physics can count on free tuition and a fellowship worth fifteen hundred dollars a year; in 1933, an outstanding graduate student of physics was grateful if he was given six hundred dollars a year, and willingly paid a third of that for tuition. A newly ordained physics Ph.D. today can reasonably look forward to a starting salary of about five hundred dollars a month in industry or the government, or, if he prefers basic research, he won't have much trouble finding an opening in a university laboratory at four hundred dollars a month; twenty years ago, there were no government opportunities for such a man, and few in industry, and unless he was very lucky, he had only one prospect — becoming a full-time assistant in a university at around two hundred dollars a month. "I'm naturally pleased to see our youngsters getting a break," Goudsmit says. "But why don't *they* act a little pleased about it? Back in 1927, I came to this country from Holland to teach at the University of Michigan. I was a Ph.D. and I was also married, and all my wife and I could afford was one room, without bath or kitchen, in a rooming house. And things really looked gloomy. Our room had two windows — one looking out on a hospital and the other on a cemetery."

It further distresses Goudsmit to see the apparent equanimity with which some of his younger colleagues regard nuclear weapons, for to him they are a frightening and ghoulishly unexpected application of atomic energy. "Several of the young physicists I've seen going off to watch bomb tests at Eniwetok or Las Vegas were as jaunty about it as if it were a holiday excursion," he says. "Some of them attend as 'observers.' Congressmen who witness the tests are given the same label, and as far as contributing to the success of the tests is concerned, I have a hunch that one set of observers is about as valuable as the other. When the young men get back — and other old-timers tell me they've noticed this, too — they're full of jolly little reminiscences about going swimming in the Pacific near dangerously radioactive reefs, and the foul-ups in the military's air shuttle, and that time out on Eniwetok when a workman spent a whole day carefully painting a dummy structure that was blown to bits the next morning. You rarely hear them so much as mention the terrible potentialities of the weapons they've seen in action. Maybe their small talk is a form of escapism, but if that's so, why don't my contemporaries talk the same way? Rabi, Bacher, Oppenheimer — a detonation leaves them awed and anxious." Dr. I. I. Rabi is chairman of the general advisory committee to the Atomic Energy Commission and a member of the Physics Department at Columbia University; Dr. Robert F. Bacher, a former member of the Atomic Energy Commission, is now at the California Institute of Technology; and Dr. J. Robert Oppenheimer, formerly director of the Manhattan District Laboratory at Los Alamos is now director of the Institute for Advanced Study, at Princeton.

Goudsmit himself has never seen an atomic explosion. "I'm like Ferdinand the Bull," he says. "I prefer to sit under a tree and smell the flowers." Actually, since the tests are not directly related to his work, he feels that he simply hasn't time for prolonged journeys to witness spectacles. "If you want to see a show, why don't you buy a ticket to 'Wonderful Town'?" he recently asked a twenty-three-year-old Nevada-bound physicist who was urging him to come along. "That might help you more with your work than going West. Pauli [Dr. Wolfgang Pauli, who is now teaching in Zurich] won the Nobel Prize by going to the theater, you know. He was watching a revue in Copenhagen when the idea for his Exclusion Principle came to him." It might be argued that Goudsmit has been to Las Vegas vicariously. In the fall of 1951, at Brookhaven, he gave a young lady scientist, who was about to set out for a Nevada test, a quarter to play for him at one of the town's casinos. On her return, she handed him seventy-five cents.

The methods by which graduate students select their schools also cause Goudsmit to feel out of step with the times. The schools that attract them, he finds, are the ones that are lavishly supplied with elaborate modern equipment. He concedes that to a certain extent this approach makes sense, for there is no denying that equipment plays an important part in scientific progress. But he suspects that the search for the latest in equipment often overshadows the search for an inspiring teacher. "Back in the twenties, we looked for the man rather than the machine," he says. "And I, at least, found the man — Bohr, of Copenhagen." Whenever Goudsmit speaks of Dr. Niels Bohr, the Danish scientist who, with Dr. Albert Einstein, is generally regarded as one of the two foremost figures of modern physics, he becomes more than ever the wistful old codger unashamedly pining for the days of his youth. Bohr, a septuagenarian now, has headed the Institute for Theoretical Physics in Copenhagen since 1920. Until 1943, when, to his relief, the British whisked him out of Nazi-occupied Denmark so that he could lend a hand to Allied research, he and his wife lived in an apartment at the Institute. At present, they live in a Copenhagen mansion, complete with greenhouse, that the Carlsberg beer family has turned over to the nation in perpetuity for the lifelong use of whatever individual the Danish government decides is the country's outstanding intellectual of his time.

"In the 'twenties, Bohr's modest Institute, on Blegdams Vej, was the physicist's spiritual capital," Goudsmit says. "All roads led to Copenhagen. Physicists fortunate enough to be invited made the pilgrimage from everywhere — Sweden, Germany, England, the United States, Russia, India, Japan. No more than twenty were ever there at one time, except when Bohr organized a conference to review the state of physics. Then the number might rise to fifty. We would drop everything when an invitation came to go to Copenhagen — just to think and talk. We would go there to have our ideas confirmed, or refined, or picked to pieces. And we would stay until that was accomplished — several days, perhaps, or several months — discussing and discussing in Bohr's study, while Mme. Bohr saw to it that we had plenty of tea and sandwiches. Our talks might last all night. Sometimes we'd do our talking over beers at the Wivel, and once, I remember, I even debated a formula with a colleague during a wild roller-coaster ride at Tivoli."

Despite the limitations in the way of equipment, the 'twenties, in Goudsmit's opinion, were heroic years in the history of atomic physics. "Bohr had written a marvelously intuitive paper on the structure of the atom, and suddenly five fat volumes of unexplained observations on spectral lines began to make sense," he says. "We were as happy as Egyptologists must have been a century earlier, when Champollion succeeded in deciphering hieroglyphics. The 'twenties were a period of such optimism that physicists every-where believed they were on the verge of explaining all the phe-nomena of the universe. One of the most eminent of them told a meeting of the Physical Society in London that soon the only prob-lem left would be what he considered a comparatively simple one — the origin of life. The physicists proved to be a little over-optimistic, of course. We are still confronted by riddles, the chief one right now being the nucleus of the atom. Who knows how long we will have to wait before another breakthrough takes place? The conditions we work under today certainly aren't hasten-ing that breakthrough. A quarter of a century ago we could ex-change ideas in Bohr's study with no government secrets, weapons programs, or spy cases to bother us. No Tex and Jinx, no auto-graph hounds. None of us were distracted by offers to become college presidents or big wheels in industry, and governments didn't give a hoot about physicists. There was no trying to elbow one's way to power, for the simple reason that there wasn't any place to exercise power. No huge laboratories, no military projects. A Rockefeller Fellowship was considered quite sufficient. We all felt that we belonged to a sort of lodge, with a worldwide member-ship of only four hundred or so, and everyone knew everyone else well — or at least knew what everyone else was doing. Now four times that number will turn up for a meeting of just American physicists, and most of them will be strangers to each other. Why are they at the meetings? Some of them, no doubt, because of a deep interest in the structure of matter. But there are also some, I suspect, who are attracted by the fact that physics has become fashionable and by the possibility of being offered a lucrative industrial job. In the days of the lodge, physicists were automatically called 'obscure' in popular publications. Now the adjective, even for the most obscure of us, is 'prominent.' "

Goudsmit's present position in the world of physics enables him to observe, and contribute to, the general tumult from many angles. As chairman of the Physics Department at Brookhaven, a post he has held since 1950, he suffers daily from many of the administrative headaches that have shattered the serenity of his calling. The job entails, among other things, hiring and firing personnel, organizing scientific projects, and sitting in as a member of a committee that decides how the nine million dollars annually allotted to the Laboratory by its parent organization, the United States Atomic Energy Commission, is to be spent. As senior scientist at Brookhaven, he is in a position to take an active part in purely scientific research and to keep abreast of the latest developments and trends in that field. Another help to him in this respect is his editorship of the *Physical Review,* to which he was elected in 1951 by the members of the American Physical Society, which sponsors the publication. (The *Review* has a circulation of eighty-five hundred and annually publishes about five thousand tightly printed pages of treatises.) In this capacity, Goudsmit, at the head of a group of outstanding physicists who act as first readers, each in his own special line, passes on practically everything that goes into the journal. His public has a high opinion of his editorial talents. "The *Review* has improved noticeably since Sam took over," Bacher said not long ago. "The job must be pretty taxing at times, but it's effort well spent. After all, the quality of research everywhere is influenced by the quality of the *Review*."

Goudsmit is an author as well as an editor. Since his student days at the University of Leyden, he has written, alone or in collaboration, two technical books, *The Structure of Line Spectra* and *Atomic Energy States,* and one that is not so technical, *Alsos,* as well as approximately a hundred papers for the *Review* and other scientific journals. Many of his papers have been significant contributions to the advance of physical science, and one of them, at least in the opinion of two Nobel Prize winners — Rabi and Dr. Enrico Fermi, of the University of Chicago — has been of fundamental importance. This describes the discovery made in 1925 by Goudsmit and another Hollander, Dr. George Uhlenbeck, who is now professor of physics at the University of Michigan, that electrons, far from being static, as had been presumed up to then, are constantly spinning. The discovery cleared up a good many questions about the structure of atoms. "It was a tremendous feat," Rabi says. "Why those two men never received a Nobel Prize for it will always remain a mystery to me."

Alsos, Goudsmit's one nontechnical work, which he wrote in 1947, is an account of a wartime experience that he feels was fantastic for a man of his background but perhaps no more so than a lot of other things physicists have found themselves doing in recent years. In the spring of 1944, General Leslie R. Groves, who was then in charge of this country's efforts to produce atomic bombs, picked Goudsmit to serve as the uniformed civilian head of a highly secret mission to Europe whose object was to find out what progress German physicists were making along the same lines. Fortunately for the Allies, as the mission discovered at some peril, the Germans were not trying to produce atomic bombs, but, of course, nobody knew that then. As a matter of fact, the scientific community here, many of whose members had learned their physics

from distinguished German enemies, was generally convinced
that its accomplishments were lagging at least two years behind
those of the Reich. Some of the scientists working in Chicago,
which was at that time the heart of our atomic-bomb research,
grew so jittery about the likelihood of a German atomic attack
that they moved their families away from the city. As it turned
out, the Germans were directing their efforts to building a uranium
pile, which they hoped to use either as a source of power or as
an explosive weapon to drop on an Allied target. Uranium piles,
however, are as big and heavy as a concrete warehouse, and even
had the Germans succeeded in building one, its value as a weapon
would have hinged on the remote possibility of figuring out a
means of transporting it to a target. By the end of the war the
Germans were no farther along in their research than the Allies
had been in 1943, when they started trying to put an atomic
bomb together. In large part, according to Goudsmit, this stupendous failure of the Reich's physicists, whose ranks included men
of the highest ability, was the fault of political meddling. "Science
should be left to scientists, but the Nazis insisted on appointing
loyal party hacks to important administrative posts," he says.
"It was a case with them of holding on to power at all costs. It is
not true that totalitarianism proceeds with matchless efficiency or
that democracy is necessarily fumbling and inept."

Goudsmit claims to be unable to understand why General Groves
selected him for the German assignment, which a number of high
government officials regarded as one of the Allies' most important
Intelligence missions. Some months after he had agreed to under-
take it, he was handed a folder of papers listing the qualifications
of several individuals who had been recommended to him as
possible assistants. As he was shuffling them about on his desk,
a memorandum that had somehow got mixed in with them fell to
the floor. He picked it up and read, "Dr. Samuel A. Goudsmit.

Has some valuable assets, some liabilities." His liabilities, he says, occurred to him right off, but he was far from sure about his assets. It seems likely, though, that General Groves made his choice on the basis of far more detailed information than was contained in that cryptic memorandum, for Goudsmit's abilities and temperament were already well known to the military. Early in 1941, he had left the University of Michigan and, after a few months at Harvard, had joined the Radiation Laboratory, a secret radar-research project at the Massachusetts Institute of Technology, in Cambridge, as editor of secret documents and acting head of a group investigating the theory of radar. This was the first time he had strayed from the insularity of academic life, and it ultimately taught him how to get along easily with an assortment of more or less worldly people. "It was a strange laboratory," he says. "I had to work with lawyers, engineers, administrators, security operatives, writers, and a charming husband-and-wife team of artists who were on leave from the Walt Disney studios to illustrate handbooks that explained our project to certain generals." In recalling this period, Goudsmit's wife, Jeanne, remarked not long ago, "Before we went to Cambridge, Sam found the ways of even chemists a little hard to understand." After Goudsmit had spent two years at M.I.T., his horizon was further broadened when, in the summer of 1943, the Radiation Laboratory sent him to England to find out why Royal Air Force crews were satisfied with their radar apparatus and American fliers using practically the same equipment were not. This involved interviewing scores of crews. Goudsmit lived with them in their barracks at various airfields, spent short leaves with them, drank with them. And he found the answer: The Americans were using the wrong kind of planes for the type of radar they were using. The American Eighth Air Force, which was then this nation's principal striking arm in England, was equipped with high-flying strategic bombers, but the radar instruments in the planes were better suited to low-flying tactical craft. Goudsmit then consulted with another physicist from the Radiation Laboratory, Dr. Lauriston C. Marshall, who had been sent to England to help set up a similar laboratory there, and the two men presented the facts at a meeting of high-ranking Air Force officers held in a Tudor mansion headquarters outside London and presided over by General Carl Spaatz. A couple of times during recesses, Goudsmit heard himself referred to in the corridors as "the long-haired Joe." "It was the closest I've ever come to feeling like inorganic matter," he has since said. Goudsmit went back to M.I.T., and the radar equipment in question was presently shifted to the low-flying tactical planes of the Ninth Air Force, which had followed the Eighth to England.

It was shortly after his return to the United States that Goudsmit was tapped by General Groves for the rather more arduous, if on the whole less fruitful, task of finding out what the Nazi scientists were up to. The mission, for which Goudsmit was later awarded the Medal of Freedom and the Order of the British Empire, was called Alsos. This was a Hellenization of General Groves' last name and was chosen by the Army as a form of camouflage, apparently on the theory that Americans know Greek and Europeans don't. Only six members of the mission, which, at its peak, numbered about a hundred, were atomic scientists; the rest were military men, women clerical workers stationed in a rear-area headquarters, and several scientists who, while they didn't know a great deal about atoms, were distinguished specialists in other fields and were taken along as another means of throwing the enemy off the scent. There is some question in Goudsmit's mind as to whether the Alsos insigne — a white Greek lower-case "A" pierced by a bolt of red lightning — did much to help preserve secrecy, but anyway there it was, with orders to stencil it on the mission's vehicles and other equipment. "I suppose it represented power, might — the great atom itself," he says. "Life in those days sometimes seemed to consist mostly of fathoming the United States Army."

Tight-lipped and furtive, the Alsos people arrived at an airport near Cherbourg and headed for Paris in a caravan of jeeps and trucks. Once there, they began asking around for Dr. Frédéric Joliot-Curie, the famous French physicist, and this, of course, tipped people off to the nature of their errand. "Complete strangers — French and American — began coming up to us and confidentially offering their assistance," Goudsmit says. "They'd assure us that they knew our work was ultra-secret and that they wouldn't breathe a word to anybody. So after a while we began to relax. It got so that if we needed special co-operation of some sort — say, for cutting red tape to get at documents or prisoners — we'd just whisper to the right general or the right sergeant, 'Atom bomb.' It always worked."

Goudsmit and the five atomic scientists assigned to him felt that their primary objective was to find Dr. Werner Heisenberg, who was Germany's outstanding physicist and one of Goudsmit's oldest friends. "No one but Professor Heisenberg could be the brains of a German uranium project, and every physicist throughout the world knew that," Goudsmit later wrote in *Alsos*. The Pentagon, however, favored action on a wider front, arguing that Hitler might have entrusted atomic-bomb research to Germans Goudsmit had never heard of. He went to some pains to explain to Washington that while the Nazi political leaders might have developed almost overnight, there was no chance of anyone's having eclipsed Heisenberg as a physicist in the comparatively brief space of time since the two scientists had last been in touch with each other. "The military men in Alsos would probably have preferred to work with more conventional Intelligence agents," Goudsmit says amiably. "Sometimes both sides had a distinct feeling of being stuck with each other."

There were numerous instances of this difference of approach to the problem. The mission was barely under way when its Pentagon advisers forwarded a laboriously prepared report on a

German scientist who had traveled extensively in the United States just before Pearl Harbor and in whom it was felt Goudsmit might be interested. "The report was all right, I suppose, as far as it went," Goudsmit says. "It told us that he liked beer, didn't care for American women, and had had German measles. It might have told us a lot more if it had gone into the matter of what kind of questions he asked our scientists." A Regular Army colonel who had been assigned to direct whatever military maneuvers Alsos might be called upon to execute became impatient at Goudsmit's lack of the spirit of adventure. One day, Goudsmit learned that the colonel had put some Alsos officers and men through a special course of training in preparation for making a parachute raid on a German laboratory that Goudsmit had reason to believe was of little importance. "His plan was to seize the files and kidnap the scientists working there," he says. "He was quite crestfallen when I sat down with him and made him see that nothing in that particular laboratory was worth one sprained ankle."

Sometimes it was the colonel who had to explain the facts of life to Goudsmit. For instance, there was the morning when word reached Alsos that Heisenberg was spending a few days in a town in Switzerland. Goudsmit wanted to join him there. Sounding out the colonel on the idea, he explained in detail what old friends he and Heisenberg were; the German had visited him in Holland way back in the 'twenties and, until Germany invaded Poland, had regularly spent his summers with the Goudsmits in Michigan. Such old friends, Goudsmit told the colonel, would naturally have a lot to talk about when they met, and almost inevitably the subject of physics would come up. While it was to be assumed that Heisenberg would discuss such matters warily, he nevertheless might say enough to give Goudsmit a lead on what headway the Germans were making in atomic research. "When I was all through," Goudsmit says, "the colonel smiled and asked me, 'And while he's giving you a lead on them, why wouldn't you be giving him a lead on us?' Frankly, I'd been so excited at the prospect of talking to Heisenberg again that I hadn't thought of it that way."

When the Americans reached the Rhine, in September 1944, some of the Alsos men waded out into the river under enemy fire and collected samples of water. These were shipped to Washington to be tested for radioactivity, on the theory that the Germans might be using the Rhine to cool a uranium pile. Just before the shipment went off, an officer considerately inserted a bottle of French wine — an excellent Roussillon — for his friends back in the Pentagon. "Test this for activity, too," he wrote on the label. A few days later, Alsos received a Top Secret Action radiogram reading, "Water negative. Wine shows activity. Send more. Action." Goudsmit, concluding that Washington was simply entering into the spirit of things, tossed the message aside. That was a mistake. The message was soon followed by another, irately demanding an explanation of Alsos' failure to comply with orders. It developed that some abstemious and literal-minded officer in the Pentagon *had* had the wine tested for radioactivity. The test had proved mildly positive, and the officer, who was unaware of the fact that many wines are slightly, though harmlessly, radioactive, owing to the composition of the soil where the grapes are grown, had jumped to the conclusion that Alsos was on the track of something big. Before matters could be straightened out, Goudsmit, not wishing to run the risk of ignoring orders a second time, dispatched one of his atomic scientists — Major Russell A. Fisher, who had been a student of his at Michigan and is now chairman of the physics department at Northwestern University — to forage for more samples of wine. "I instructed Fisher not to be stingy with the confidential funds," Goudsmit recalls. The Major's tour of southern France was a triumph. Wherever he appeared, he was fêted with radioactive wine by French vintners, who assumed that he was taking advantage of his Army status to build up postwar business relations with French exporters. He rejoined the mission with a large and representative collection of Rhône wines, samples of grapes and soils, and vials of water taken from various small French rivers. "His bibulous wanderings must have given him courage," Goudsmit says. "The report he sent Washington after that trip was so outspoken on the subject of rear-echelon interference that from then on the Pentagon cut its efforts to direct us by remote control to an absolute minimum."

With the capture of Strasbourg in November 1944 four German scientists fell into Alsos' hands. They were uncommunicative, and, former colleagues though they were, Goudsmit ordered them interned, but their files, which were found in a laboratory at the University of Strasbourg, contained information showing that while the Nazis had a uranium project under way, its progress to date was inconsequential. Heisenberg, the papers revealed, was working in a German village called Hechingen, and his laboratory there, which was the Reich's closest approach to an Oak Ridge, took up only one wing of a small textile factory. Goudsmit's elation at this news is recorded in *Alsos,* in which he quotes himself as having exclaimed to another member of his mission, "Isn't it wonderful that the Germans have no atomic bomb? Now we won't have to use ours."

As Alsos pushed on into Germany, the seizing of more physicists, laboratories, and documents corroborated the evidence at Strasbourg. Still, as long as Heisenberg remained at large there could be no certainty. Shortly before the troops reached Hechingen, in April 1945, high American and British Intelligence officers came from Washington and London to be in on the kill. When the Alsos forces burst into Heisenberg's office, all they found there was a large framed photograph on the wall, showing its missing occupant and Goudsmit. The picture had been taken in 1939, while the two were enjoying their last summer together in Michigan. "The military men laughed about that photograph," Goudsmit says. "But they were also puzzled. I could have helped them out, I suppose, but that didn't seem quite the moment to explain about the lodge."

Heisenberg, who had abandoned his poorly equipped laboratory and sought refuge in the Bavarian Redoubt, was found near Munich a few days later, and taken to Heidelberg, where Goudsmit was waiting for him. "It was impossible for me not to greet my old friend warmly," Goudsmit says. "Purely on impulse, I asked him, 'Wouldn't you like to come to America now and work with us?' And he replied, 'No. Germany needs me. If you and your American colleagues want to learn about the uranium problem, I'll be glad to show you the results of our researches. But you will have to come to my laboratory.'"

On August 6, 1945, Goudsmit was poking about alone among the ruins of Himmler's headquarters in Berlin when an American officer hurried up to him and said that a special plane was waiting at the Tempelhof Airport to take him to Frankfurt, where Alsos then had its headquarters. The pair raced through Berlin in a jeep with screaming sirens, were waved through the Tempelhof gate without formalities, drove out onto the field, and stopped beside the plane, whose propellers were already turning. "I climbed from the jeep into the plane, the door slammed shut, the motors roared, and we were off," Goudsmit records in his book. "It was just like the movies."

In Frankfurt, Goudsmit found a two-week supply of fresh laundry waiting for him, but, welcome surprise though that was, it seemed unlikely to him that he had been rushed from Berlin simply to enjoy it. He asked the colonel what was up, but the colonel, who was ordinarily communicative enough, on this occasion evasively muttered something about somebody or other who might or might not arrive from Washington. Goudsmit spent the evening in an associate's apartment chatting with a group of Alsos people he hadn't seen in months, and shortly before midnight he drove one of them, a secretary, to the hotel where she was billeted. The lobby was empty except for a bored sergeant on duty at the desk, who was listening to a dance band on a portable radio. As Goudsmit was saying good night to the secretary, an announcer broke in on the dance band with a special bulletin: An atomic bomb had been dropped on Hiroshima. "That was the reason they'd shanghaied me out of Berlin," Goudsmit says. "The city wasn't zoned off yet, and our military thought that when the Russians heard the news, they might kidnap me. Well, anyway, the music came back on the radio, and the secretary started asking me all sorts of questions about atoms. I answered calmly, but I didn't feel calm. I was angry that the military should have been in a position to keep me in the dark about so momentous an event involving my science. But, standing in that lobby in Frankfurt, I realized that much more of the same thing was in store for physicists in the years ahead. And I realized, too, that the days of the lodge were over."

$$* \quad * \quad *$$

Goudsmit got his first tantalizing whiff of physics at the age of eleven. Alone and bored one afternoon, in his parents' comfortable, middle-class house in The Hague, where he was born, he flipped open a textbook of elementary physics that belonged to his older sister, and hit upon a passage describing how the science of spectroscopic phenomena had proved that the stars are composed of the same elements as the earth. "Hydrogen in the sun and iron in the Big Dipper made Heaven seem cozy and attainable," he says. At that time, however, physics did not occur to him as an eventual vocation. Millinery did. His mother owned a fashionable hat shop called Au Louvre, on the Prinsestraat, in The Hague, and from the time he was ten she consulted him regularly before deciding on new models for her clientele. "That one ought to have a flower instead of a feather," the boy would say, and more often than not his mother and her designers would agree that he was right. "I found the talk of styles and Paris entrancing," Goudsmit recalls. "Even now, when I think of Parisian streets and buildings, I can hear my mother's voice telling me about them. And then there was the excitement of guessing six months in advance what kind of hats Dutch ladies would want next. Both the risk and the romance of the business appealed to me greatly."

Goudsmit was in his last year of high school when his mother had to abandon Au Louvre, because of poor health. His father, Isaac, was a prosperous wholesale dealer in bathroom fixtures, but this business did not interest the boy at all. His only impressive grades at school were in science and mathematics, so, in 1919, for lack of any other signpost, he enrolled as a physics student at the University of Leyden, ten miles from The Hague. He began his studies with misgivings. His first love was still millinery, and he felt that in his case physics could lead only to a lacklustre career of high-school teaching; he didn't think he was up to meeting the stiff requirements for a professorship in some European university, which was then about as far as a physicist could hope to get. At Leyden, though, his reluctant embrace of physics soon turned to devotion, as he came under the influence of the late Paul Ehrenfest, a professor of international prominence. A less astute teacher might not have become aware of Goudsmit's talents, for they were of an unorthodox nature. Unlike most students of physics, he seemed to base his thinking on empirical hunches rather than on logical and analytical grounds, and he possessed an almost uncanny intuition, comparable perhaps to his ability to forecast Dutch ladies' taste in hats. "Sam always had a fanciful imagination," Dr. Walter F. Colby, director of Intelligence for the Atomic Energy Commission, who was responsible for bringing Goudsmit to this country, has said; and Dr. George Uhlenbeck, a fellow-student of Goudsmit's at Leyden and at present a professor at the University of Michigan, once told a friend, "As physicists go, Sam was never a conspicuously reflective man, but he had, and has, an amazing talent for taking random data and giving them direction. He's a wizard at cryptograms, and it's not hard to understand why." Rabi has also noticed this maverick strain in his make-up. "Sam has a sixth sense when it comes to bringing order to jumbled facts," he says. "He thinks like a detective. He *is* a detective."

Actually, Goudsmit would have the jump on the next man should he ever want to become a detective in the ordinary sense of the word. While studying at Leyden, he had a job on the side for a while as a research assistant at the University of Amsterdam, where he heard that the local police chemist was giving a course in detective techniques. He signed up for it, and for eight months learned how to compare fingerprints, spot forgeries with ultraviolet light, and analyze various types of stains, such as those made by blood and grease. "Taking that course was one of the most sensible things I ever did," Goudsmit says. "I learned a detective's attitude toward the evaluation of evidence. It's been extremely helpful in my work." And, blandly ignoring the tributes paid to his intuitive powers, he adds, "People usually go too much by intuition, without judging what's in front of them."

While at Leyden, Goudsmit also joined the Christian Huygens Society, a student discussion group. The members took turns giving half-hour talks on various cultural topics. Goudsmit's topic was always the same — the structure of the atom, and this caused a falling off of attendance at the meetings he addressed. The society's president finally asked him to find something else to talk about. Goudsmit was baffled. He felt that all he knew was the atom. Determined not to let the president down, he enrolled in a course in Egyptology. When he appeared in the classroom on the opening day of the semester, he found he was the only student there. "Three make a lecture — God, teacher, and student," the professor, an ancient, kindly gentleman began, intoning a Latin proverb, and Goudsmit was embarked on the study of Egyptology. He stayed with the course two years and, with an alacrity that brought joy to the heart of his lonely teacher, learned to decipher hieroglyphics.

The professor was eager for him to go into this subject more deeply, but instead Goudsmit turned to collecting scarabs. "The professor considered that vulgar, but the reality of the scarabs made me feel closer to Egypt than the printed hieroglyphics I'd been working on," Goudsmit says. "It's odd that I've never been there, but it's not because I haven't tried. Some years ago, I attempted to set up a cosmic-ray experiment in which the Pyramids would be used as absorbers. I wanted to put Geiger counters both inside and outside them to gauge the rays' powers of penetration. But the project fell through. Another time, while I was teaching at Harvard, I made friends with an Egyptian student of mine, and he said that when he got home his first act would be to get the University of Cairo to invite me there as a lecturer. I gave him an A in the course, and then the scoundrel went and married an American girl and settled in Boston."

Under Ehrenfest's direction, Goudsmit made excellent progress at the University of Leyden. His second year there, when he was only eighteen, he produced a treatise, based on his own research, that dealt with the spectroscopy of alkali doublets. "A most presumptuous display of self-confidence but a highly creditable paper," Uhlenbeck recently said of this early effort. Other papers followed, and they were climaxed in the summer of 1925, two years before Goudsmit received his Ph.D., by one he prepared with Uhlenbeck, describing their discovery of the electron spin, a contribution of fundamental importance to the quantum theory; without it the magnetic properties of matter cannot be adequately explained. The electron spin has since become so taken for granted in physics that students today are inclined to believe it was revealed in Genesis, but at the time it was what physicists needed to clear up an enormous number of riddles involving the structure of the atom. More than one winner of a Nobel Prize has drawn heavily on the findings of the two young Leyden scholars in working out the contribution to science that earned him the award.

With the publication of the electron-spin theory, both its authors were established as important physicists. Goudsmit was invited to attend discussions at the Institute for Theoretical Physics, in Copenhagen, which was headed by the eminent Dr. Niels Bohr, and he was subsequently awarded a Rockefeller Fellowship, which he used to study in Germany; while there, he joined forces with Dr. Edmund Back, a German scientist, and the two men succeeded in measuring the spin of the atomic nucleus, the first time this had ever been done. In 1926, Colby, who was touring the Continent as a talent scout for the University of Michigan's Physics Department, visited Leyden and, on Ehrenfest's recommendation, signed up Goudsmit and Uhlenbeck as instructors. Goudsmit was engaged to Jeanne Logher, a former designer in his mother's shop, and he felt that the relatively high teaching salaries offered in the United States were a factor that a young man who was about to assume domestic responsibilities was in no position to ignore. Moreover, the opportunities for academic advancement were considerably greater here than in Europe. The idea, however, had its drawbacks. For one thing, he hated to leave Ehrenfest. For another, he hated to leave Europe and its "string-and-sealing-wax era." Ehrenfest minimized both objections. "I'd advise you to go," he said to Goudsmit. "American physics may disappoint you at first, but the science is building up there. Always watch the slope of the graph. It's not where a thing is at the moment that counts but where it's going." In the summer of 1927, Goudsmit, now a married man, moved with his bride to Ann Arbor.

At Michigan, some of the time Goudsmit was accustomed to devote to research was taken up by the unfamiliar task of teaching, but he found that this did not make him nearly as unhappy as he had feared. In fact, he soon came to look upon teaching as a welcome new aspect of his career. In his spare hours, he continued his study of the atomic structure, writing numerous papers and two books on the subject, but, valuable as his findings were, none were as spectacular as the spin theory. This did not surprise him. On the eve of the spin theory's publication, Ehrenfest had warned him that just such a letdown was likely to follow, and in 1931, while Goudsmit, then twenty-nine, was delivering a guest lecture at the Sorbonne, he referred to himself, more or less facetiously, as a "has-been." He has since elaborated on this phenomenon. "As a physicist's career goes, it was to be expected," he says. "A scientist can do useful work all his life, but if he is to carry learning one big step forward, he usually does so before he is thirty. Youth has the quality of being radical, in the literal sense of the word — of going to the root. In science, as in other fields, youth seems to be the time when one is driven to examine the roots — the basic assumptions of everything that has previously been accepted. Obviously, if one hits on something through this approach, it may well be outstanding. After a scientist passes his creative peak, it seems to me the most useful thing he can do is teach the status quo to youngsters, who may then attack it with all their irreverent curiosity and so perhaps arrive at fresh knowledge. Teaching gives older scientists the same satisfaction as parenthood — the sense of self-renewal."

This fairly abstract satisfaction was not the only one that Goudsmit derived from teaching. Somewhat to his astonishment, he discovered that he also enjoyed the homely, day-to-day routine of academic life. He liked the company of his students outside the classroom as well as in it. Friday nights, he held open house for them, with his wife acting as hostess. "They'd bring their dates, and the girls and I would fix pancakes and later wash the dishes together," Mrs. Goudsmit recalls. Goudsmit's first candidate for a Ph.D., Robert F. Bacher, who later became a member of the Atomic Energy Commission, remembers that during his final year at the university he spent three hours or more every day simply hashing things over with his teacher. "We talked not only about physics but about Egyptology and life in general," Bacher has since said. "I've observed a great deal of teaching in the more than twenty years since I left Michigan, and I believe Sam is probably one of the two or three best lecturers in the profession." Goudsmit's ways in the classroom were far from formal, if a report of an episode at Columbia, where he taught a summer-school class shortly after the war, is any indication. According to Rabi, who, no matter what the season, is usually busy in his laboratory on Morningside Heights, Goudsmit was proctoring an examination one suffocating August afternoon when, glancing out the window, he saw an ice-cream vender in the street below. Silently invoking the honor system, Goudsmit left the room. Ten minutes later, he returned with thirty popsicles and put one on each of his perspiring students' desks.

Goudsmit has some fairly strong feelings about the teaching of physics. He thinks, for one thing, that the textbooks most teachers use stress applied science over theory to an appalling degree. More than once he has heard a teacher tell students that diligence in laboratory work will make them handy at repairing mechanical gadgets at home. He summed up his opinion of this approach to the subject during a symposium at Harvard in 1950: "I can only say that I have taught elementary, intermediate, and advanced laboratory work to undergraduates and graduates for many years and . . . I still am unable to do anything helpful around the house." Goudsmit feels that even when teachers do stress theory they tend to resort to homespun analogies that are misleading; in discussing radio waves, for example, a teacher will usually draw a wavy line on the blackboard and mention the surface of the ocean, although actually radio waves and water waves have nothing in common. "To some teachers an atom is always a ball," he says. "In the winter it's a basketball, in the spring it's a baseball, and the rest of the time it's a ping-pong ball. The atom is no more explained by such images than the idea of God is by a picture of an old man with a long beard sitting on a cloud."

Some years ago, a student of Goudsmit's at the University of Michigan wrote a letter in which he made an earnest attempt to give a friend of his an idea of his teacher's classroom technique:

> Dr. Goudsmit started his lecture today with the usual serio-levity with which he approaches his almost futile effort to impart even a cursory grasp of physics to dull engineers. He made the routine cracks about the inefficacy of the "prehistoric" demonstration apparatus, and wandered playfully around the darkened lecture room snatching spectra, which were being produced by a machine on the lecture table, with a small screen held in his hand. Presently, however, he became serious and began to talk about atomic theory. His accent thickened slightly, and his voice became a bit louder. He spoke with a trace of negligent reverence of those colleagues of his who had contributed vastly to the great mass of modern scientific knowledge — Bohr, Einstein, and the like. His enthusiasm mounted as he explained how new concepts evolved into satisfactory theories with the help of classical physical manipulations. Philosophically, he discussed the pitfalls man has encountered in trying to resolve the most basic puzzles of nature in terms of "wire models and ping-pong balls" and with great humility he accepted man's impotency and insignificance. He was eloquent! When the bell rang, he stopped abruptly in the middle of a thought, as though awakened from a trance, smiled wryly at the stupid dolts pulling on their coats, and disappeared through the door at the rear of the lecture platform.

The fact of the matter is that, unfortunately, few scientific concepts are reminiscent of wire models, ping-pong balls, or anything in everyday life, and Goudsmit is pretty much resigned to the belief that it will probably be a long, long time before the general public begins to get so much as a glimmer of what the physicists who influence their destiny are talking about. He feels, however, that this is no valid reason for the tendency — more noticeable in the past, perhaps, but still in evidence — for scientists to live apart from other people. As an example of this tendency, he recalls the time he drove down to Princeton in the winter of 1948 to visit his old friend Uhlenbeck, who had spent the preceding six months or so at the Institute for Advanced Study there. After discussing physics for a few hours in Uhlenbeck's quarters, the two men went over to the Institute's lounge for tea and sat down at a table no more than a yard away from one at which Goudsmit thought he recognized T. S. Eliot, the poet and dramatist. "George started talking physics where we had left off a few minutes before," Goudsmit says. "But I broke in and asked him if the fellow at the next table wasn't Eliot. He said it was, and that Eliot had been at the Institute for the past two months, working on a play. The two hadn't even nodded to each other when we went in, and I thought that was strange. 'Haven't you and he ever met?' I asked George, and he looked mildly surprised and said no, they hadn't. There was nothing unusual about that, he assured me, since the scientists at the Institute and the people studying arts there rarely mingled, and he pointed to several tables in the lounge at which scientists were clustered and then to some others at which there were only people in the humanities. What a wretched situation it was, I thought, that two men of such enormous curiosity as George and Eliot could spend a couple of months in the same small community and never even get around to passing the time of day."

In the summer of 1938, while traveling in Europe on a Guggenheim Fellowship, Goudsmit returned to the Netherlands, where the University of Amsterdam offered him the professorship he had once thought he was incapable of attaining. The offer was tempting, but by then he felt too firmly established in the United States to make the switch. He was a full professor of three years' standing at Michigan, and he had a comfortable house in Ann Arbor and a five-year-old daughter, Esther, who was already beginning to acquire American ways. Esther, now a junior at Smith, looks back happily on her childhood in Michigan. "There were always people in the house — either students or scientists," she says. "I. I. [Rabi] and Uncle Enrico [Fermi] and all the others would sit around in a circle, discussing and discussing. I never understood what they were talking about, of course, but I felt sure they did, because they all seemed like such fine men."

The excursion to the Netherlands gave Goudsmit his last opportunity to visit his parents. The next time he entered his family's house in The Hague, he was the uniformed civilian head of Alsos. In the summer of 1945, after beating his way across France and into Germany, Goudsmit made a side trip to The Hague, but he knew when he parked his dusty jeep outside the family house that he would not find his father and mother there, for he had learned from captured German records that, being Jews, they had been gassed two years earlier in a Nazi concentration camp. The house was a shambles. Everything made of wood — doors, walls, moldings — had been torn down and burned as fuel during the Occupation. "Climbing into the little room where I had spent so many hours of my life," Goudsmit wrote in *Alsos,* "I found a few scattered papers, among them my high-school report cards that my parents had saved so carefully through all these years. If I closed my eyes, I could see the house as it used to look . . . Here was the glassed-in porch which was my mother's favorite breakfast nook. There was the corner where the piano always stood. Over there had been my bookcase . . . The little garden in back of the house looked sadly neglected. Only the lilac tree was still standing."

After four years of war service, most of it secret and technical, Goudsmit found the prospect of resuming his placid existence at Michigan hardly satisfying. His realization that he did not want to go back there came to him on the evening of December 10, 1945, while he was having dinner on a train with Dr. David Dennison, an old friend and colleague of his at Ann Arbor, whom he had not seen since 1941. The two men, both of whom had errands in Washington, had boarded the train at Trenton after attending a party given at Princeton in honor of Wolfgang Pauli, who had just received the Nobel Prize for his Exclusion Principle. As they sat in the dining car, Goudsmit was enjoying the reunion immensely when Dennison, who was chatting about faculty doings at Michigan, happened to remark that he had some good news for him — Goudsmit was going to be granted a wish he had made in 1937. In the spring of that year, Goudsmit, who was spending most of his time in research and was teaching only a few graduate students, had told the head of the Physics Department that if and when the opportunity arose he would like to devote himself solely to teaching elementary courses to undergraduates. His feeling at the time was that he was done for as a research man because he hadn't an adequate mathematical background, and that teaching first-year physics was the next-best thing to retirement, which he couldn't afford. Now, eight years later, Dennison was telling him that the opportunity he had asked for was awaiting him. To his amazement, Goudsmit realized suddenly that he no longer wanted it. "I can see in retrospect how childish it was of me, but that evening I found myself wondering how David could think I would possibly be interested in teaching undergraduates at a Midwestern university," he says. "I'd returned only recently from overseas, and I suppose I hadn't yet got things back into their proper perspective. Anyway, I had the feeling that it was my duty to take an active part in scientific developments in order to — yes, at the time I perhaps even meant it literally — to help save the world. I had the illusion then of — well, of having grown considerably. I felt caught up in the violent upsurge of everything associated with physics that had followed Hiroshima, and I wanted to be more closely associated with it than seemed possible on a university campus. In a modified way, I still feel the same about a physicist's obligation to society, but in 1945 I went overboard on the subject."

It took Goudsmit some time to figure out how to translate his rather vague feelings about obligation into some form of positive action. He wasn't even sure that his decision on the diner had been a sound one, and, while groping for a solution to his problem, he joined the faculty of Northwestern University, in Evanston, Illinois, in the hope that a change of scene might revive his interest in academic life. But after a year of it he was still, in his word, "restless." In the spring of 1948, he received an offer to join the staff at Brookhaven as senior scientist and, after some soul-searching, accepted it, for there, he hoped, he could not only continue his research and teaching but would have a hand in the elaborate scientific enterprises that were sprouting up all over the nation. "It was a straddling maneuver, my coming to Brookhaven," he has since said. "I imagined that it would spare me the decision of choosing between the old and the new." It might be thought that he swung both feet on the side of the new when, in 1950, he became chairman of Brookhaven's Physics Department, and thus assumed a heavy burden of administrative worries, but in theory, at least, he is still straddling, for he has not relinquished his post as senior scientist, which offers vast opportunities for pure research — if he only had the time.

In taking on his additional duties, Goudsmit was, of course, well aware that he would have to give up much time that he would like to devote to research, but by then he was convinced that in view of the current trends in science he could do no less. The military was moving in on the physicists. Government and industry were investing huge sums of money in the profession. Decisions affecting the whole future course of physics were being made by men who in many cases were not the best qualified to make them. Some of these men had never got beyond teaching science to high-school students, and others weren't scientists at all. Then, too, Goudsmit had observed that certain excellent physicists were proving themselves first-rate administrators — instituting efficient research techniques in their organizations, cutting through red tape whenever it threatened to hamper the scientists working under them, and discreetly handling senators with an itch to pry into what goes on in government laboratories. "That interested me," Goudsmit says. "It seemed to demonstrate that there might be an art to administering, that one might learn to guide without commanding. I now know that this is true, but I also know that many researchers who haven't yet come around to seeing it that way are taking an intellectually snobbish attitude toward administering that isn't helping the situation any. It's the same sort of snobbery that makes young physicists feel they won't get ahead unless they use the title of 'Doctor.' As if titles meant anything — except when it comes to airline-reservation clerks. They're the only ones I use my Ph.D. on. It guarantees me a seat, because they always figure I'm a physician dashing off on an emergency call."

The friendliness Goudsmit displayed toward his students during his teaching days was not, as is sometimes the case, a calculated pedagogic device for charming them into an interest in his subject; his geniality is as definite a part of his nature as his intuitiveness, and it helps to make him something of an exception among physicists. He had not been at Brookhaven long when a reactor expert paid a call on him and, upon leaving his office, was heard to exclaim in astonishment to a colleague in the corridor, "That fellow Goudsmit! He talks physics, but he talks a lot of other things, too. Gives you the feeling that we've been infiltrated by a layman." Mrs. Mariette Kuper, who is executive assistant to the director of Brookhaven, feels much the same way. The wife of Dr. J. B. H. Kuper, who is chairman of the institution's Department of Instrumentation and Health Physics, she regards physicists as pleasant and human enough, on the whole, but rather like members of a religious order. "They go around talking their special language, like monks in India," she says. "Sam talks the language the rest of us talk." Mrs. Regina Brown, who is Goudsmit's administrative secretary, has found working for him an unusual experience. "I'd heard he was an important scientist, and that made me kind of nervous when I started out," she recently said. "I got a real surprise during my first few days on the job. While I was getting acquainted with the files in the office, I found several transcripts of technical addresses he had delivered, and saw that the recording stenographer had typed in the word "laughter" in parentheses after a good many of the sentences. I could hardly believe my eyes. Most physicists are just walking brains, but he's different. He's more interested in people. A lot of the young men around here — and the older ones, too — come to him for advice about their personal problems. They ask me if Mr. Anthony or the Great White Father can see them, and he somehow makes time for them." Dr. Edward O. Salant, a well-known cosmic-ray man of Brookhaven, puts it differently. "Sam's rather peculiar for a physicist," he says. "Most of us are just as sensitive as he is, but to inorganic matter rather than to people and their private worries. Our work isn't concerned with life. It doesn't involve us with the sort of emotions that physicians and people in business see so much of, so if there's anything to Shaw's claim that man becomes like his work, it's only natural for us to be pretty inept when we're confronted with human problems. I envy Sam, in a way, but personally I regard the world as essentially a convenient platform for a cosmotron."

As for Goudsmit himself, he is unaware that his outlook differs much from that of other physicists. He believes that physicists are no less capable of experiencing human emotions than any other group, but he concedes that what stirs their emotions may be rather different. As he sees it, achievement arouses affection in a physicist, and he cites as an example his own feeling toward a notoriously bad-mannered but exceedingly brilliant scientist. "He's a mean, caustic, and boorish man," Goudsmit says. "I once dined with him in a restaurant and he hounded the waiter until the poor fellow got so nervous he dropped his tray, and that made my friend howl with glee. To most people, he would be *persona non grata*. To me, he is a man who has solved difficult scientific problems, and in my home, he is welcome."

In Goudsmit's dual capacity at Brookhaven, he is constantly plagued by the feeling that no matter what he is doing at any given moment, he ought to be doing something else. "Before the bomb, contemplation was the physicist's stock in trade," he says. "It's a luxury now." His only moments of calm come in the early morning, before the day's problems begin. He tries to leave his home, a stucco house in Sayville, in time to reach his office ahead of the rest of the staff, so that he can have a few minutes of solitary reflection to strengthen him for the long hours ahead. He makes the half-hour trip to Brookhaven in an aging Oldsmobile, and finds the drive exhilarating. "It gives me the virtuous illusion that I'm exercising," he says. The sight of armed guards at the entrance to the institution is slightly disturbing, he admits, but once they have let him by, he forgets them as he looks about at the neatly laid-out grounds and finds solace in the reminiscent names of its thoroughfares — Princeton Street, Cornell Avenue, Columbia Street. If, as he nears Building 109, a plain, one-story wooden structure in which he and his assistants have their headquarters, he finds the adjacent parking space empty, he is cheered. "No good mornings to say, no telephone bells ringing or tyewriters banging," he explains. Entering 109, he makes his way down a short, still corridor, and, unlocking its door, lets himself into his unpretentious office. At this point, he takes a deep, satisfied breath and feels ready to tackle the day's work. But at the thought of work his energy and confidence die. "At that instant, my day begins to disintegrate," he says. "I don't know where to start. All sorts of projects crowd into my head. The morning has fooled me again. A moment before, my office seemed a citadel, but now it has become a trap — a maze with countless passageways that I must explore all at once."

A blackboard that stands in front of Goudsmit's desk — all physicists think with chalk — does nothing to restore his peace of mind. Its upper right-hand corner, where he has scrawled the day's schedule, is crammed with disparate commitments that make his head swim. By way of an antidote, he is likely to tell himself that this may be one of the days when two physicists who are engaged in improving a mass spectrometer that he conceived in broad out-line, in 1948, will burst into his office with the news that they have ironed another wrinkle out of their working model. Goudsmit has told them that, regardless of what he is doing, they are to break in on him the minute they have any progress to report. "That spectrometer is one of the few projects I'm involved in nowadays that give me the feeling I'm a scientist," he says. When the spec-trometer is finally ready for use, it will be more compact than and one-tenth as expensive as any other model, and, what is more important, it will weigh heavy atoms with greater accuracy. While Goudsmit prefers to think of his spectrometer as an instrument that will be primarily useful in basic research, he is not oblivious to the fact that an industrial engineer who recently visited Brook-haven expressed the belief that it may prove valuable in refining oil and analyzing gases. The possibility of a substantial reward from industry, much as he could use it, confuses him. "Money and engineering have diverted us to the point where I don't know if we're gadgeteers or scientists," he says. "There are easily three times as many physicists now as there were before the war, but only ten per cent of them are in the fields where important dis-coveries are made. The bomb showed so-called practical men that physicists aren't necessarily vague long-hairs, and now they won't let us alone."

Sooner or later, of course, Goudsmit has to turn his attention back to his blackboard. On a typical day, one of the notations on it may remind him that he has called a meeting of the group leaders in his department for three that afternoon. He does not expect it to be as exhausting an administrative session as the one at which the nine million dollars that the Atomic Energy Commission appropriates to Brookhaven every year is budgeted, but touchy considerations are bound to arise. Some extra money has been allocated to the Physics Department, and the heads of the ten branches of the department — High Energy Physics, Nuclear Properties, Solid States Studies, and so on — will have a lot to say about how it should be apportioned. It will be up to Goudsmit, as chairman of the department, to make the final decisions and fend off the brickbats of the men who feel that they didn't get a fair share. This is a position most administrators find themselves in from time to time, and Goudsmit does not enjoy it, but then, as he often points out, he never did think that he would whole-heartedly enjoy being an administrator.

Goudsmit's cherished solitude ends when one of his two secretaries comes in and puts the morning's mail and a cup of coffee on his desk. The coffee cup, a gift from his staff, has a whip painted on its side — a little intramural joke testifying to his easygoing nature as a boss. Sipping his coffee as he goes through his mail, Goudsmit may find a couple of pieces of particular interest. One may be a research paper from his old friend Fermi, submitted to him as the editor of the *Physical Review,* the semimonthly publication of the American Physical Society. Although Goudsmit has a board of distinguished scientists and a clerical staff of four to assist him in editing the *Review,* the job could consume his entire working day if he allowed it to, and sometimes it seems to him that he has enough to do without it. But this morning the job is a joy, for it gives him the opportunity to be one of the first to read the results of Fermi's newest research.

The other item of interest in the mail may be a long memorandum from the Navy describing in detail the educational backgrounds of four outstanding young engineering officers who have been selected to study nuclear physics under Goudsmit at the Massachusetts Institute of Technology, where he gives a four-week course each year. Its aim is to prepare officers for later training in nuclear engineering, which, it is expected, will eventually enable them to direct the operation of submarines run by atomic energy. "I try to wean them away from the engineering handbooks they've been raised on," Goudsmit says. "Those manuals are anathema to a physicist. They're answer books without questions. The principal spur to scientific thinking is doubt about the answers and a desire to remove that doubt, so I try to teach them the questions and make them wonder if the old answers are really the right ones. Well, they're bright, eager young men, but so far I can't say that they have become exactly weighed down by doubts. But perhaps that's all for the best. I've put in for a dive on the first atomic submarine, and if I get to go along, I sincerely trust there won't be any doubt about surfacing."

Fortified by his coffee, Goudsmit tackles the blackboard again, but at this moment his telephone may ring. Possibly the call is from an Intelligence official in Washington who wants to discuss the advisability of letting a certain German physicist work on an American atomic project. Goudsmit's experience in Germany during the war has made him an authority on such matters. Assuring the government man that he will call back, he opens the combination lock of a cabinet near his desk and plows through his files for the necessary information. The files are full of documents he accumulated in the course of the Alsos mission — Himmler's dossier on underground laboratories, for instance, which was found in Munich, and Göring's budget for atomic research, a souvenir of

Göttingen. Frequently while he is rummaging about in the drawers, he lingers over another accumulation — a box containing the hundred or so scarabs that he has collected since his Leyden days. One of his favorite pieces of Egyptology is a worn clay figure of a pregnant hippopotamus, representing Toueris, the goddess of fertility, and as he runs a thumb over its smooth back, he may turn to gaze at lithographs on the wall that show the Temple of Karnak and people drinking tea on the terrace at Shepheard's. "I love my scarabs because they remind me that there is a life beyond the world of physics," he says.

After Goudsmit has called Washington back, a secretary may place on his desk a bulky security report, its cover stamped "CON-FIDENTIAL" in large red letters, that concerns a candidate for a physicist's job with the Atomic Energy Commission. Goudsmit is a member of the three-man Personnel Security Board for the Commission's New York district, which checks on scientists against whom security charges have been made. The reports submitted to the board are exhaustive, and Goudsmit generally finds that reading them takes more time than they are worth. "So many of them fall into the category of men who have an in-law who has, or had, Leftist connections," he says. "Frankly, after three years on the job I've just about concluded that the screening process is far less likely to catch a Fuchs than to hurt many innocents. That man Fuchs! Harmful as he was to the free nations, he was even more harmful to science. So many travel restrictions now keep scientists of different countries from getting together to talk science — the science of nature's secrets, I mean, not governments' secrets. We need each other's ideas or our research will run dry."

At last, Goudsmit takes a good stern look at the blackboard, and notes that a brand-new physics Ph.D. who would like to work at Brookhaven is due in exactly three minutes. He has allowed the young candidate half an hour, which, he realizes, may be excessive. It won't be if the applicant is the diffident sort of man who is hard to get to know but who may well have the makings of a valuable scientist. On the other hand, if he turns out to be one of those smooth and garrulous opportunists who a generation ago would have scorned the idea of struggling along with string and sealing wax but who now regard physics as the coming thing, Goudsmit will find the half hour far too long. The chances are, though, that the young man will not fit exactly into either classification but will be the mystifying composite of visionary scientist and well-adjusted citizen that the universities are turning out nowadays, and that Goudsmit finds intensely difficult to relate to anything in his previous experience. In the corridor outside he can hear the secretary and the Ph.D. approaching, and, rising from his chair, he spends his last seconds of privacy rearranging the cast of his mind in order to present the proper front. "At times like that, I wish that I felt sick," he says. "Just sick enough, that is, to go home and go to bed and do some serious thinking about my mass spectrometer — or even sort out my scarabs — while the Long Island fog closes in around my bedroom windows. But then the door to my office opens, and there's no escape."

A DEACON AT OAK RIDGE

MOST SCIENTISTS, like most other people, are too preoccupied with their daily work to ponder its moral implications, but those who do sometimes reach fairly sweeping conclusions. Certain physicists, for example, won't have anything to do with military projects; others, equally conscientious in their self-searching, feel that at the present time they would not be justified in trying to do anything but make atomic weapons more lethal. Extreme as both positions may sound, the one that has recently been taken by Dr. William G. Pollard, the executive director of the Oak Ridge Institute of Nuclear Studies, in Oak Ridge, Tennessee, is, for a man of science, even more radical. After twenty years as a physicist, during which his philosophic point of view has been just as objective and just as skeptical as that of any of his colleagues, Pollard has been ordained a deacon of the Episcopal Church. A week before Christmas, 1952, at the age of forty-one, with his four sons serving as acolytes, he was invested with holy orders in ceremonies held at St. Stephen's Church, in Oak Ridge — a building he had helped put up with his own hands. His ordination came at the end of two and a half years' intensive study of theology, culminating in an examination that he found more rigorous than any he had taken as a graduate student at Rice Institute, in Houston, Texas, while preparing a doctoral thesis entitled "On the Theory of Beta-Ray Type of Radioactive Disintegration." "I think my theological examiners wanted to be certain I wasn't just pulling an intellectual stunt," Pollard says.

Working simultaneously as a physicist and as a religionist, Pollard has found, leaves him practically no free time. Most of his weekdays are spent supervising the affairs of the Institute, a scientific alliance of thirty-two Southern universities that operates on an annual budget of about two million dollars, which is put up by the federal government, but on Sundays, wearing his vestments, he is busy at St. Stephen's, where he assists at Holy Communion. In addition to carrying on his work with the Institute, he has for several years been engaged in secret military research; nowadays, upon returning home from a conference at a certain Oak Ridge war plant where he has presented his latest findings in connection with this project, he may don his clerical dress and pay a pastoral call on some ailing and frightened elderly parishioner. Some time ago, having read a paper on "The Separation of Isotopes by Gaseous Diffusion" at a scientific meeting at Ohio State University, he stayed over a day to address three hundred members of the university's business school on "Revelation and Response."

Pollard says that he has no interest in trying to reconcile faith and skepticism. He considers them mutually antagonistic, and has chosen faith, in which, as he puts it, "explanations are useful but not necessary." "I no longer believe that the approach of size-up-and-solve will produce a formula explaining all natural phenomena," he says. "If this sounds like heresy to any of my scientific colleagues, I can only say that the more I have learned of science, the more I have become convinced that the origin of the universe will forever remain a mystery to us. And I say this with sympathy for those who disagree with me, for, like them, I have been an agnostic who was sustained for many years, and happily so, by the hope of that master formula. Ten years ago, I would have been incapable of taking the step I have taken. Wars, social upheavals, nationalism — I once reacted intellectually to such things, but now I see them as perhaps containing elements of God's judgment. I'm less worried now about these problems than I used to be — though not because I have any greater confidence in man's being able to cope with them."

A year or so after he had been ordained, I visited Pollard in Oak Ridge, and far into the late hours of a mild Southern night listened to his account of how he had arrived at his religious decision. We sat talking on a narrow wooden porch outside his house, which overhangs a gully filled with pines and dogwoods, while from time to time his wife, Marcella, a spirited woman with an oval face and hazel eyes, made us comfortable with highballs of Tennessee sour-mash whiskey. "After Bill's ordination," Mrs. Pollard said, with a smile, as she brought in a round of drinks, "a Hard-Shell Baptist wrote him that he shouldn't have picked a denomination that lets its ministers drink." She sat with us most of the evening, rarely speaking and periodically looking in on her four sons, who were reading and listening to the radio in the living room. Occasionally, one or another of the boys, who range in age from twelve to nineteen, joined us for a brief period. At first, I ascribed these appearances to curiosity about an unfamiliar guest, but, watching them as they listened intently to their father, I gradually came to suspect that they were still curious about his having adopted a second career; Pollard, I discovered, has never been able to give a specific explanation for it. "I'm fuzzy when it comes to reasons," he told me, "and I've heard them all, including the one that I may have deliberately overstated a position that many scientists have informally come around to. But I'm serene about the decision itself, and that's what really counts."

Pollard is a rather good-looking man, with a high forehead, brown hair, a thin nose, and inquisitive gray eyes, and he is, of course, well educated. (He has five degrees, two of them honorary.) There is nothing sanctimonious about him; he talked to me with candor, and there were times, indeed, when he discussed his new status with open amusement. Pollard told me that he was born in Batavia, New York, and that when he was twelve his family moved to Knoxville, Tennessee, where his father, who had been a mining engineer, became the regional representative of an electrical-equipment firm. Pollard was brought up in the Episcopal faith, but he lost interest in it as a high-school student and turned to the Unitarian Church. After three years he also gave that up. By the time he married, which was in 1932, shortly after graduating from the University of Tennessee, he had come to look upon religion as, in his phrase, "a fairy tale." "To me, it seemed to be a matter of Bible fundamentalists insisting that Adam was the first man and that the world was created in 4004 B.C.," he told me. "I was by then immersed in my graduate work at Rice and I didn't see how anyone could fail to realize that the only rational way for us to make the best of the universe was to comprehend its material nature."

His bride, Pollard went on, held an opposite view. Her parents, who were Presbyterians in Nashville, had brought her up as a regular churchgoer (she became an Episcopalian while a student at the University of Tennessee), and she was determined not only to remain a regular churchgoer but to bring up any children she might have in the same fashion. "In the early days of our marriage, we had many crises over that," Pollard said. "Three months after our wedding, I remember, Marcella very much wanted me to go to church with her one Sunday, but I told her that the studying I was planning to do at home was more important. The church was a mile away, and she told me later that as she walked toward it alone, she kept looking back, hoping that I would be trying to catch up with her. I was doing no such thing, but neither could I get any work done as I sat at home thinking of her. And since I couldn't, I figured that one of us might as well have our way, so after that I went to church with her. But I wouldn't say the Creed. I considered it too ridiculous."

In 1936, with a Ph.D. in physics from Rice, Pollard returned to the University of Tennessee as an assistant physics professor. Five years later, he was an associate professor and two years after that a full professor. He was also the father of four little Episcopalians — baptized in that church at his wife's insistence — but he was far less interested in their religious upbringing, he told me, than in his research. In 1944, he was asked to join Columbia University's Special Alloys and Metals Laboratory, which was a cover name for one of the wartime Manhattan District's most important scientific units. He did research there on the gaseous-diffusion method of extracting U-235 — the explosive in atomic bombs — from common uranium. Moving to New York meant two months' separation from his family, who had to remain in Knoxville until he could make arrangements to bring them here, and during that period he lived in the King's Crown Hotel, on Morningside Heights, not far from the Pupin Physics Laboratories, at Columbia University, where his unit was then situated. Even without his wife to act as a spur, Pollard said, Sunday as often as not found him in church; he wasn't sure whether he went there just as a matter of habit or in order to provide cheering items for his letters to his wife, who was concerned about the logistics of moving their children and furniture to New York. When his family at last arrived here, he told me, he was relieved, because that meant he could once again assure himself that he was attending church simply in the interests of domestic accord. "I saw myself as just a father taking his wife and four small boys somewhere on Sunday morning," he said.

"We moved into a fairly nice house in Mount Vernon," Mrs.

Pollard recalled. "Bill became a commuter. By that time, the Laboratory had been moved to the old Nash automobile building, on Broadway at 133rd Street. It was quite a far cry from the campus at Tennessee."

Although in the course of his work, Pollard had occasion to visit the then secret city of Oak Ridge, where there was an enormous gaseous-diffusion plant, he and his associates at Columbia were told no more than was necessary about what was going on and knew nothing of the successful atomic-weapons test that took place in New Mexico on July 16, 1945. They did, however, know that something was brewing and they were therefore not quite as surprised as most people when, three weeks later, President Truman announced that an atomic bomb had been dropped on Hiroshima. "I was exhilarated," Pollard said. "I was in the Nash building at the time, and my colleagues and I kept the radio going all that afternoon and took turns rushing out for the latest editions of the newspapers. We finally knew for certain that our work had been effective." Three days later, he continued, when the Nagasaki bomb was dropped, his mood changed. Mrs. Pollard shifted restlessly in her chair at this point, and her husband, after glancing over at her, went on to explain, "Marcella doesn't want me to say what I'm about to say."

"You know how people are," Mrs. Pollard said. "They'd think Bill turned to the church because of a sense of guilt."

"They'd be mistaken, I believe," Pollard said. "But whether they'd be right or wrong, I don't see why that should keep me from talking about a meaningful experience." He hesitated briefly, and then resumed where he had left off. "After the Nagasaki bomb, my exuberance was replaced by something approaching terror," he said. "I thought the bombs would be sprinkled all over Japan. When I got back to Mount Vernon that evening — it was a Thursday — I picked up a newspaper and saw on the religious page that I had just enough time to get to a service in New Rochelle. I walked out of the house alone and took a trolley to Trinity Episcopal Church there. This time, there were no little boys along. As the service progressed, I became conscious of a feeling that it wasn't just an empty rigmarole, and when I got back home, I was no longer disturbed. I slept calmly that night."

Shortly after V-J Day, Pollard said, he returned to the University of Tennessee. He had not been there long when he heard a physicist, Dr. Katherine Way, at a party in Knoxville, outline an idea that stirred his enthusiasm, as well as that of several others present. Now that the war was over, she suggested, it would be a fine thing if university researchers in the Oak Ridge region could use some of the elaborate facilities there, which were far beyond the means of any school. Her suggestion led to a conference of Southern scientists in December, 1945, at which Pollard was chosen chairman of a committee whose purpose was to sound out federal and academic officials on the idea. After months of scurrying about between Washington and various campuses, the committee succeeded in winning both government backing for the project and the sponsorship of fourteen leading Southern schools, and the Oak Ridge Institute of Nuclear Studies was well on its way. In October 1947 the sponsors appointed Pollard executive director for a five-year term, and he thereupon resigned from the Tennessee faculty. Two months later, the Pollards set up housekeeping in Oak Ridge.

If he and his family had moved to a more settled community, Pollard told me, he might never have taken holy orders. "At best, I might have wound up a good, solid Episcopalian," he continued, smiling. "But Oak Ridge was only five years old and its churches had little or no resources. It was hard not to lend a hand, but if you did, you let yourself in for more than you'd bargained for." However, Pollard's first concern at Oak Ridge was to organize the Institute, and to judge by its growth, he would appear to have accomplished this effectively; the number of its academic sponsors has more than doubled in its first six years, and its staff, which at first consisted only of Pollard, an administrative assistant, and a secretary, totals a hundred and seventy-five. The Institute trains scientists from American and foreign universities, medical schools, and industrial firms in the use of radioisotopes, or "tracer atoms"; it provides the facilities for scores of university teachers to do research; it awards Atomic Energy Commission fellowships to young physicists to study the latest methods of guarding against radiation hazards; and it operates a thirty-bed hospital and a laboratory for the study of the effects of radioactive materials on cancer.

It was plain to Pollard that the local Episcopalian affairs were just about as badly in need of spadework as the infant Institute. He and his fellow-parishioners had no church building; like the members of several other sects represented in Oak Ridge, they worshipped in a high-school gymnasium. One Sunday, as he and his family were leaving the gymnasium after the morning services, he casually inquired of the rector, the Reverend Stephen Davenport, if he thought the parish would ever have a church of its own. Davenport replied that only a few days previously he had received word that the Atomic Energy Commission was about to allocate land to the various denominations that wanted their own churches. Then the Rector startled Pollard by inviting him to head a drive for a building fund. "I could have pleaded pressure of work, I suppose, but since I was the one who'd brought up the matter, I didn't see how I could back down," Pollard told me. "Anyway, I took the job on, and we raised eight thousand dollars."

In August 1948 the church's Sunday-school superintendent and lay reader, an engineer named John Bull, left Oak Ridge to study for the ministry. A month later, the Rector, perhaps recalling Pollard's diligence as a fund-raiser, asked him to fill Bull's Sunday-school post. "I wanted to turn him down," Pollard said, "but I had four children going to Sunday school — more than most of the parishioners — so I was stuck. Now that I look back, practically all the steps that led to my ordination seemed just temporary and inconsequential at the time." As Sunday-school superintendent, Pollard led a fifteen-minute service for the whole student body, which numbered about a hundred, and afterward, like ten other volunteers, taught a small class. He found that the questions his pupils asked in class made teaching unexpectedly interesting. "The children wanted to know things like how various feast days came into being and why we have Lent and where this or that canticle came from," he said. "Since I didn't know, I had to read up on the subjects at the library. I was amazed at how absorbing the material was."

That fall, the persuasive Davenport gave up his post in Oak Ridge to become rector of a church in Massachusetts, and he was presently replaced by the Reverend Robert F. McGregor. McGregor also proved to be persuasive. Inquiring around for likely nominees to fill Bull's position as lay reader, he was told by several of his parishioners that their children were enthusiastic about Pollard's Sunday-school services. Impressed, McGregor asked Pollard how he would feel about becoming a lay reader. "He made it sound so easy that I wonder why he needed anyone," Pollard told me. Lay reading, the Rector explained, merely meant reading the appropriate prayers from the Book of Common Prayer at morning or evening services; if Pollard agreed, McGregor would arrange with the Bishop of Tennessee to have him licensed as a lay reader. "I agreed," Pollard said, adding, with a shrug, "It was another of those steps."

As a lay reader, Pollard told me, he enjoyed leading prayers but found the contents of the prayers themselves even more rewarding. As he grew increasingly familiar with their wording, he began to wonder about their origins. Accordingly, just as he had done in response to the questions of his Sunday-school pupils, he embarked on a reading program, but this one was on a formidable scale. He bought books — dozens of them — and spent all his free hours studying them. From time to time, glancing at his bookshelves, he would find himself smiling at the incongruous juxtaposition of his worn scientific volumes with such titles as *Early Traditions of Israel, Source Book of Church History for the First Six Centuries,* and *Doctrine of the Trinity.* His reading program gave him an entirely fresh view of the Bible. "I'd previously taken it at its face value," he said, "but now I discovered that it was a highly complex blending of independent literary sources that were fascinating to disentangle. Here was a field of bona-fide scholarship that commanded my intellectual respect, without which, I imagine, I couldn't have embraced religion. It was exciting to find that the Bible didn't have to be accepted solely on the basis of its philosophical and metaphysical values. It could be accepted as a piece of history describing the unique fortunes and experiences of a people, which culminated in the revelation of God among them. Through the Bible, I now saw, the Judaeo-Christian civilization could be studied in the same disciplined way as, say, the Greco-Roman civilization. In fact, one Hebrew writer — theologians differ over his identity, but I believe it was Ahimaaz, the son of a priest of David — impressed me as being much more truly the father of history than Herodotus. If I'm ever at a university again, I may learn Hebrew, so that I can read the work in the original."

Pollard was happily persevering at his private research when, in June 1950, Davenport and Bull returned to Oak Ridge for a sentimental but formal occasion; Bull had completed his training for the ministry and had asked Davenport to preach the sermon at his ordination. In his sermon, Davenport pointed out that, like Bull, many lay readers had gone on to prepare themselves for the diaconate — an order of the ministry, just below the priesthood, that carries with it the privilege of assisting at Holy Communion and, if the deacon is licensed to do so by the bishop, of preparing and delivering sermons. "Listening to him, I gathered that the duties of a deacon were only slightly greater than those of a lay reader," Pollard said. "The training, I knew, took three years at a seminary under ordinary circumstances, but I'd already read so extensively in church history and liturgics that I felt I must have already completed some of it. The idea of having my religious studies organized, as my scientific studies had been, appealed to me. Anyway, I thought, there'd be nothing final about deciding to study for the ministry. I'd have to be admitted first as a postulant and after that as a candidate for holy orders, and I could always quit at any time along the way. I'd say that my approach then was more curious than dedicated."

For a few weeks after the visit of Davenport and Bull, Pollard said, he talked over the idea of studying for the ministry with a close friend — a biochemist in cancer research at the Institute — who also had leanings in that direction. "It was an odd time to be discussing such matters — just when the Institute was coming along so wonderfully," Pollard observed to me. Then, one evening, McGregor came by the Pollards' house on church business of an unrelated nature, and when it had been disposed of, Pollard brought up the subject of preparing for ordination. McGregor remarked simply that he had suspected his lay reader might be contemplating such a step. "He was letting me know that the decision had to be my own," Pollard told me. Shortly thereafter, Pollard and the biochemist began meeting at regular intervals with McGregor, who mapped out a program of study for them, and late in 1950 they were admitted as postulants. The biochemist dropped out in April 1952 because he could not afford the time, but Pollard, although he, too, was busy, stayed on. "I became deeply interested in the curriculum," he said. "Marcella and I cut our social life to the bone. If I had to go out of town for the Institute, I studied on the train or plane, and in my hotel room."

"Bill's only recreation was doing carpentry and rolling asphalt walks for the church we were building," Mrs. Pollard said. "And even that stopped in the middle of 1951, when St. Stephen's was finished."

A year after Pollard started his formal studies, he was admitted to candidacy for holy orders. That was in October 1951. Three months afterward, he took the first part of the examination required for ordination as a deacon at the Episcopal rectory in Maryville, a few miles south of Oak Ridge, before a Board of Examining Chaplains that consisted of two of the most learned theologians in the diocese. For an entire day, they questioned him exhaustively on the subjects of the Old and New Testaments, liturgics, and such branches of practical theology as homiletics, pastoral care, and pastoral administration. Two days later, he received a letter informing him that he had acquitted himself well and could go on preparing himself for the second — and final — part of his examination.

Pollard said that the deeper he got into religion, the more frequently he found himself uneasily comparing its point of view with that of science. He discovered that it wasn't easy to relinquish the secular beliefs that he had relied on for so long. "Each time I was about to tackle a new aspect of religion, I'd be sure there was going to be something in it that I wouldn't be able to swallow," he told me. "Dogmatic theology, I remember, had me especially worried." Eventually, after a trying period of several months, he succeeded in reaching certain conclusions that, while many scientists would undoubtedly consider them false, enabled him to cross the line between mere curiosity and dedication. "I decided that a person could, without violating his intellectual integrity, both think within the framework of a Judaeo-Christian view and believe all scientific knowledge of the structure of the world," he said slowly. "I decided that science was a way of investigating the wonders of

God's creativeness, such as the marvelous unity of a living cell and the intricate combinations of particles that make up matter. That being so, it seemed to me irreligious to oppose the work of science."

But while this reasoning made it possible for a religious man to be a scientist, Pollard pointed out, it scarcely bridged the philosophical chasm between the two fields — between the religious view that man is a creature of God, dependent on Divine Providence, and the view, implicit in much of science, that everything in the world as we know it is dependent upon prior sets of conditions, which we need only to understand and place in their proper sequence in order to control the future. Thus, Pollard said, a leading educator has declared that a complete science of psychology would make it possible for us to become "masters of our souls as we are now masters of heat and light." Pollard smiled as he let me ponder the implications of that thought, and then he dismissed it by saying, "That's about as likely as a carbon atom explaining the solar system." During this period of introspection, he went on, it occurred to him that physics itself, like other sciences, has its share of paradoxes, a fact that would seem to disprove the theory that all phenomena can be arranged in a neat pattern based on cause and effect. As an example, he cited the famous argument that scientists got into a quarter of a century ago over whether light is composed of electro-magnetic waves or particles; each side, accepting the premise that there could be only one true concept of the atom, assembled convincing data with which to discredit the other. In the end, Dr. Niels Bohr, the Danish physicist, showed, by means of his principle of complementarity, that while the two concepts were contradictory, both were essential to an understanding of physical phenomena. "As many scientists are beginning to recognize, the more knowledge we accumulate, the clearer it becomes that science is unlikely ever to lead us to an orderly arrangement of nature's ways," Pollard said.

"And certainly our scientific achievements haven't affected our freedom of will to use them for either building a utopia or destroying civilization. I have come to interpret events as revealing the acts of God — an interpretation that I know the single-minded scientist will have nothing to do with, because I can't prove it. But isn't one look at the armed world today enough to suggest that he, with his conviction that increased knowledge means progress, is also guilty of some sort of faith?"

Expect for a few intimate friends, Pollard said, he had planned to tell no one what he was up to until he had passed his examination. Two weeks before the second part of his examination, however, he changed his mind. A quarterly meeting of the Institute's board of directors was coming up, and he felt that the members — a group of nine distinguished educators and scientists — were entitled to advance warning about the possibly controversial step he was hoping to take. At the meeting, which was held in a walnut-panelled room in one of the Institute buildings at Oak Ridge, the board disposed of several items on the agenda and then the chairman asked Pollard to leave the room. "That was when I had to speak up," Pollard told me. "I knew they were about to take up my reappointment. So I said to them, 'There's something you ought to know,' and then I told them what I'd been doing and what I was planning to do. I said that while I didn't think it would affect my direction of the Institute, I was aware that the denominational universities among the sponsors might object. If I was ordained, I said, I would make it a point to wear clericals at the Institute only when my pastoral duties made it necessary, which would be infrequently, because that might annoy some of the other scientists. I said that I didn't want to leave the Institute but that I'd understand if they asked me to. And I suggested that if they wanted me at all, they might reappoint me for just a year, rather than for the maximum five years, and see how things worked out. When I had finished, no one said a word, and I could sense an embarrassment among the members that I was afraid would prevent a free-and-easy discussion. I hoped someone would say something, and finally, to my relief, one of the directors asked me if I thought my position would be any different from that of other laymen who devote some of their time to church work. I replied that I didn't think so. Then I was again asked to leave the room, and in five minutes they called me back. They'd voted me a five-year term and a raise."

In November 1952, two and a half years after his Sunday-school pupils had asked him their first questions, Pollard appeared again before the two examining theologians at Maryville. They interrogated him — this time for two days — about church history, moral theology, dogmatic theology, and the history of religion. A few days later, he was informed that he had successfully completed his studies. His ordination was set for Ember Wednesday, December 17th, in St. Stephen's. At the end of November, happening to be in New York on Institute business, he dropped in at the J. M. Hall vestments shop on West Fortieth Street and had himself fitted for a clerical vest and collar. "I looked in the mirror and felt pretty good," Pollard said.

St. Stephen's Church was crowded for Pollard's ordination. Three bishops were on hand, including the Bishop of South Carolina, who had been rector of the church in Houston that Mrs. Pollard had so much wanted her husband to attend twenty years earlier and who now delivered the sermon. The presence of the four Pollard boys as acolytes gave the traditional ceremonies an unusual family touch, which was somewhat blurred by the fact that the idea of a nuclear physicist's taking holy orders attracted several reporters, as well as photographers who punctuated the proceedings with the click of cameras. Numerous Oak Ridge scientists were in the church, and Pollard suspected that it was the first time some of them had been in any church. Dozens of employees at the Institute left their desks to watch their chief being ordained, although it meant that they would be docked half a day's pay. After the ceremonies, Pollard was the guest of honor at a luncheon given by the women of the parish, and more pictures were taken. "If I'd anticipated all that fuss, I might have been scared off from the whole thing," Pollard told me.

The resulting newspaper stories and pictures brought Pollard scores of letters and telegrams from all parts of the country. Some of them were not wholly friendly. Several complained about his choice of a denomination. Others warned him against attempting to insinuate scientific cant into religion. A Midwestern well-wisher called his act proof that science was at last waking up to the true meaning of cosmic rays. One correspondent thought it a shame that a man of Pollard's education should surrender himself to the rigid rituals of the church. "Scientists who don't surrender themselves to research techniques that are just as rigid run the risk of sloppy data," Pollard remarked to me mildly. The day after the ceremonies, he discovered that, as an inverted Faust, he was in a position to make money out of his ordination when a garrulous executive of a television network in New York called him up and urged him to fly north to take part in a program. "I agreed, then wondered why, and turned him down," Pollard said. "That wasn't exactly the sort of redemption I'd been seeking." Soon lecture-circuit managers were imploring him to take to the road under their banners, and magazine editors were making him impressive offers for a first-person story describing in detail how he had met God while walking in a garden. "They all had the same hell-fire-and-damnation yarn in mind," he said. "I was to be a disillusioned scientist who felt guilt-ridden about the bomb but was finally saved by a sudden revelation of God."

In Oak Ridge itself, Pollard continued, nearly all the people who talked to him about what he had done commended him for it, but he could not always be sure whether they meant it or were just being polite. Some of the felicitations, he said, were less welcome than others — especially those of certain churchgoers who, in his opinion, looked upon religion as fashionable and therefore an asset to their social life. "I must say I hadn't thought of the ministry in that way," he said. He was also not impressed by a brother-clergyman who, at a diocesan meeting, treated him rather airily for having been "so tardy in seeing the light." "Such fatuousness isn't likely to help religion," Pollard said. Some of his scientific colleagues said nothing about the matter; he presumes that while several of them indubitably regard him as a renegade, the others simply feel it's his business, and not theirs. Pollard told me that one scientist did try to badger him one evening while they were listening to a concert of records at the home of a friend, by rather pointlessly ridiculing the Trappists. "I suppose you might call it just a coincidence, but Bach's 'St. Matthew Passion' was being played at the time," he added.

Encounters of this sort faded into insignificance when Pollard heard a rumor that one of the ranking medical officials at the Institute was considering resigning in protest against his ordination. According to Pollard, this man, a gifted researcher, is so outspoken about his antipathy toward religion that someone once referred to him as the founder of the First Evangelical Atheists' Church of Oak Ridge. "He was not only important to the Institute but someone I admired as a friend — and also, frankly, for his bluntness," Pollard said. "I dropped everything and went to see him. We talked for two hours." It turned out that the man was upset because he was afraid that his professional colleagues throughout the country would infer that the Institute was dominated by religious influences, and therefore might begin to suspect the value of its medical work. "He was apparently afraid of being found guilty by association," Pollard observed wryly. "After he got it all off his chest, I reminded him that I was the same fellow who had collaborated with him on a paper that was just about to ap-

pear in a technical journal. I assured him several times that I
had no intention of misusing my directorship, but that I had to
insist on my right to live my own personal life as I saw fit. If
he doubted my word, I said, it was his duty to bring the matter
up before the board of directors. He told me he didn't want to
do that, because he respected me as a scientist and it might mean
that I'd be fired. I realized then that since neither of us wanted
the other out of the Institute, we were going to be able to patch
things up." And eventually the medical man agreed to stay on,
but not before he had diagnosed Pollard's mental attitude as that
of a man suffering from a type of aberration that not infrequently
afflicts those who have reached the age of forty. "He told me I
could read it all in William James," Pollard said, with a chuckle.
"And I replied that since my new point of view showed me that
he was clearly living in an illusory world, the best thing for us
to do was regard each other as mentally ill and continue to col-
laborate on research."

As a deacon, Pollard has undertaken a variety of new tasks.
He gives occasional sermons at small missions in Tennessee hill
towns that cannot afford their own preacher. He assists McGregor
at Sunday services, and also at Wednesday-evening Holy Communion, to which, at the end of his workday, he goes directly
from the Institute. If McGregor is out of town — on church affairs
or on vacation — Pollard acts as the pastor of St. Stephen's, leading the congregation in worship and conducting burial services if
the need arises; occasionally at such times his two careers cross
paths. Once he was hurriedly summoned from a meeting of the
board of directors at the Institute to baptize a dying newborn
child. There are also pastoral calls to be made at the Institute's
cancer hospital, a place Pollard used to be interested in primarily
from the administrative point of view. "It felt strange, the first
time, to be wandering around that familiar ward in my clericals,"

he told me. Even when McGregor is on hand, Pollard is called upon every now and then to pay a pastoral visit. Not long ago, for instance, a neighbor of his, an elderly woman who was going to have an operation, sent word by her niece that she wanted to see him. For two weeks, Pollard stopped in daily to pray with her. He also prayed with her twice in the Oak Ridge general hospital, just before and just after the operation was performed.

Unlike the majority of scientists, Pollard said, his parishioners are not in a perpetual state of intellectual ferment, although among them are a number of people of high intelligence, including a few scientists. The core of their attitude, it seems to him, is an acceptance of what he calls "the drama of existence" — a feeling of being swept along by a force over which they have no control. "They think in terms of responsibilities, hopes, decisions, and an eventual necessity to account for everything they do," he said. "To men who spend most of their time on formulas and equations, such matters do not seem of paramount importance. Naturally, scientists are not untouched by them, but they tend to dismiss them whenever possible as unruly and trifling, if sometimes puzzling, impositions upon their orderly scheme of things. After all, how can you subject a hope to external verification? As one theological writer has said, the scientist's approach to life differs from that of the religious man as much as a sociologist's approach to women differs when he is preparing a treatise on women and when he is marrying one. After I ceased to be wholly dependent on the scientific approach, I lost the feeling that all phenomena must be explained. Now when I see a thunderstorm brewing, for example, I am able to regard it with a sense of wonder, if you will, and let the next fellow worry about air currents, temperature changes, and the rest of the physics going on up there."

While Pollard feels that nowadays he can take external verification or leave it alone, he still has a wholesome respect for the workings of the intellect. "After all, I'd be out of work if I didn't," he said. He believes, indeed, that he himself is far better suited to theological scholarship than to the more temporal aspects of church work, and it is to scholarship — which, as he reminded me, attracted him to the church in the first place — that he is devoting most of his attention. Not long after he was ordained, he spent all his spare time for three months preparing a series of twelve lectures on the Old Testament, which he delivered at weekly intervals at St. Stephen's, before audiences that included many people who were not Episcopalians. (According to McGregor, whom I met briefly before leaving Oak Ridge, few professors of theology could have done better.) At present, Pollard is assembling and editing the writings of the Hebrew historian Ahimaaz, which he expects to bring out as a book, with a long, analytical preface. In June 1953, the *Christian Scholar,* a quarterly published by the Commission on Christian Higher Education of the National Council of the Churches of Christ in the United States of America, ran an article by him on the place of science in religion; he is now a member of the journal's editorial board. He gave up eleven days of his vacation in the summer of 1953 to conduct a seminar on "The Teaching of the Natural Sciences in Relation to Religious Concepts" at Pennsylvania State College; the course was attended by twenty-six college and secondary-school teachers of natural sciences from all over the country. Half the members of the group were biologists and the rest physicists and chemists in about equal numbers.

More than a year having passed since Pollard's ordination, he is now eligible for the priesthood. He does not know whether he will go on to it. "I have a great attachment for the Institute, but it's established now, and no longer the challenge it once was," he told me. "And I often regret the amount of time it prevents me from giving to theology. I guess the relationship between man and the universe has come to interest me more than the one between nucleons and mesons." Pollard thinks more and more scientists will sooner or later come around to the same point of view. He would like to help them do so, but he suspects that he is not quite ready yet to be a proselytizer, because "too many new slants on religion are still hitting me." He believes that science is now at the pinnacle of its influence, and in the years ahead will give way to a religious renaissance comparable in its impact on the world to that of quantum mechanics in the past few decades. The perilous state of man's affairs, he feels, will be only partly responsible for this. "It just happens that there are several theologians of great stature alive today — men with far more gifted minds than their predecessors of the past century," he said. "As their ideas filter down, many scientists may come to realize that the world they think they are investigating simply does not exist."

As for himself, Pollard is uncertain what he will do. Perhaps he will remain at the Institute, perhaps he will teach physics at a denominational school, perhaps he will get out of science entirely. "Of course, I do have a family to support," he said, bowing amiably in the direction of his wife and then nodding toward the door of the living room, which was now empty. The boys had long since turned off the radio and gone to bed. The treetops below us in the gully were black and still. "We'll see, we'll see," Pollard said, rising. His wife shook her head incredulously as she and her husband showed me out. "And all I ever hoped was that maybe Bill would go to church Sundays," she said.

A-63-5